The poetry of Shakespeare is everywhere in his works. Whether it speaks the poet's own deepest thoughts in the inward drama of the sonnets or encompasses the vast sweep of man and history in the plays, there is no comparable voice. From the richness of Shakespeare's writings, a distinguished poet has made a brilliant selection. All the lyrical and dramatic uses of poetry are illuminated here: the songs, witty, gentle, or mockingly tender, that define a character or intensify a mood, the passages that sweep readers through time and space. These, with a generous and well-chosen group of the sonnets, make a matchless volume.

Mr. Frankenberg's introduction provides a penetrating analysis of Shakespeare's poetry, and Nonny Hogrogian's sensitive etchings bring an added dimension of beauty to a book that will be read and treasured for years.

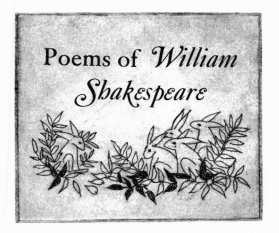

Poems of *William Shakespeare*

Poems of *William Shakespeare*

Selected by Lloyd Frankenberg

Etchings by Nonny Hogrogian

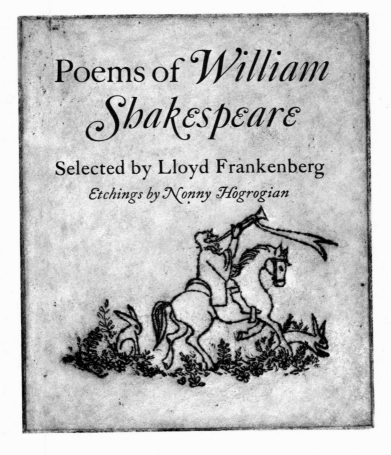

THOMAS Y. CROWELL COMPANY   NEW YORK

1 2 3 4 5 6 7 8 9 10

Contents

The Crowell Poets

Under the editorship of Lillian Morrison

POEMS OF WILLIAM BLAKE
Selected by Amelia H. Munson

POEMS OF ROBERT BROWNING
Selected by Rosemary Sprague

POEMS OF STEPHEN CRANE
Selected by Gerald D. McDonald

POEMS OF EMILY DICKINSON
Selected by Helen Plotz

POEMS OF RALPH WALDO EMERSON
Selected by J. Donald Adams

POEMS OF JOHN KEATS
Selected by Stanley Kunitz

POEMS OF EDGAR ALLAN POE
Selected by Dwight Macdonald

POEMS OF WILLIAM SHAKESPEARE
Selected by Lloyd Frankenberg

POEMS OF ALFRED, LORD TENNYSON
Selected by Ruth Grenier Rausen

POEMS OF WALT WHITMAN
Selected by Lawrence Clark Powell

POEMS OF WILLIAM WORDSWORTH
Selected by Elinor Parker

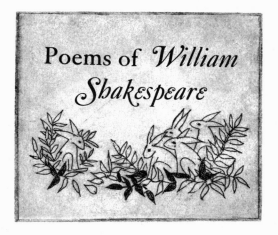

Poems of *William Shakespeare*

An Introduction to W. S.

ll that can really be told about William Shakespeare is the inside story. The outside, the recorded facts, are meager.

A child by that name (or Shakspear or Shakspur—the Elizabethans were not noted for consistent spelling) was born at Stratford-upon-Avon in 1564, the third of the eight children of John and Mary (Arden) Shakespeare. (Possibly the Forest of Arden in *As You Like It* is so named in honor of his mother.)

John Shakespeare was a merchant and occasional town official, with the privilege of having his son educated at grammar school. There William could have acquired somewhat more than the "small Latin and less Greek" rather condescendingly allowed him by Ben Jonson in an otherwise eulogistic poem. But the only documented facts about these years at Stratford are that in 1582, when William was eighteen, he married Anne Hathaway, some seven or eight years his senior, and that they had three children: Susanna, Hamnet and Judith.

The famous legend that around 1586 Shakespeare fled to London to avoid arrest on a charge of poaching has no more basis in fact than the Parson Weems fable about

I

George Washington and the cherry tree. By 1592 his name was being mentioned as an actor-dramatist and by 1594 nine or ten of the plays bearing his name had been completed. From then until his retirement in 1613, twenty-seven or -eight more are said to be by him. (*The Two Noble Kinsmen* is thought to have been a collaboration between Shakespeare and John Fletcher, who may also have had a hand in writing *King Henry the Eighth*.)

Writers of plays were paid little money or attention in those days. Shakespeare's comparative prosperity came from being a shareholder in his company, the Lord Chamberlain's (later the King's) Men, probably assisting in its management. One suspects, from Hamlet's advice to the Players in the second scene of Act Three, that he may have directed as well as acted in his own plays: "Speak the speech, I pray you, as I pronounced it to you, trippingly on the tongue; but if you mouth it, as many of your players do, I had as lief the town-crier spoke my lines."

There is a curious legend that Shakespeare stammered. In *As You Like It* the bit part of the old servant Adam, which Shakespeare is said to have played, contains such lines as "Most true, I have lost my teeth in your service" and "I scarce can speak to thank you for myself." It is even alleged that he is making wry allusion to this in the succession of *m*'s beginning Sonnet 116: "Let me not to the marriage of true minds / Admit impediments."

Three years after his retirement to the substantial house he had bought in Stratford, Shakespeare died, aged fifty-two, on the day that is customarily taken to be his birthday, April 23. Much has been made of the fact that in his will he left his wife "the second-best bed." According to the likeliest conjecture, it was the one she customarily slept in.

Since no manuscript in Shakespeare's handwriting exists, there is no absolute proof that he is the author of the poems and plays attributed to him. This has given rise to all sorts of speculation. Literary sleuths have produced (or invented) clues to "the true author" as being, among many others, Christopher Marlowe, Francis Bacon, Edward de Vere (Earl of Oxford), even Queen Elizabeth.

However, the style of their known writings, including the queen's (she did compose a few ditties), would scarcely qualify any one of them. In the absence of contrary proof, it seems reasonable to conclude that Shakespeare wrote Shakespeare. Nearly all of his plays, it is true, involve characters in disguise, but their identities are always revealed in the end. If, for whatever reason, someone had used Shakespeare's name as a mask, he would surely have disclosed himself to posterity. For, as the sonnets will make plain, one of his dearest ambitions is to realize his own decidedly original idea of immortality.

I'm not sure how one should begin reading Shakespeare. I only know the two ways I began were wrong. One was to be started off on Charles and Mary Lamb's *Tales from Shakespeare*. That was like a subscription to *Reader's Digest*. Why go back to the original article when you already know the plot?

The other was quite the reverse. In school we studied the "great speeches," like Portia's "The quality of mercy is not strained" in *The Merchant of Venice*, and soliloquies such as Hamlet's "To be or not to be, that is the question." The suspicion grew that the plays, if I should ever read them, would be all huge blockbusters of verse hurled at each other by characters who, as soon as they were on their own, went about talking to themselves. If these were the best parts, keep us from the rest.

How was I to guess that the excitement had died out in them, that they were logs dragged from the fire? The more we examined these specimens, the more it was like putting a stethoscope to a valentine, or a microscope to the jawbone of a dinosaur.

No, poems and plays are to be read in full; then, if you will, analyzed. If pleasure precedes study, study will augment the pleasure. But it can do no harm, indeed it may be helpful, to lead up to the complex pleasures of a play by way of the simpler, self-contained poem. It is only from individual poems that we arrive at an idea of poetry.

If this book were to be called *The Poetry of Shakespeare*, it would have to be printed from microfilm. For of course the poetry is everywhere. The problem would be what to leave out, like finding a poor restaurant in Paris. Exhaustive research might produce two very slim, practically useless but fascinating guides-in-reverse: *How to Eat Badly in France* and *The Worst of Shakespeare*.

The poetry might be thought of as the fabric, the whole cloth out of which Shakespeare fashioned particular plays and particular poems. The analogy is far from exact: he did not first mill the goods and then cut patterns from them. The two acts were one and the same.

And yet there is a continuity; call it a vein or, better

yet, a pervasive rhythm flowing from play to play, from poem to poem, which we come to recognize as the Shakespearean style. This style too varies—in weight, in tone, in color, in texture—as he puts it to comedy, to tragedy, to historical drama. And as these various styles mature they become first suppler, more pointed and direct; then more condensed, encrusted, allusive, dazzling and profound.

Even *The Poems of William Shakespeare*—a title that might have simplified the choices—would have resulted in a book too unwieldy for its purpose: to introduce Shakespeare as a poet to readers unfamiliar with him. His lengthy exercises in "classical themes," *Venus and Adonis* and *The Rape of Lucrece,* and the cryptically beautiful "The Phoenix and the Turtle" may be left for later reading. Other poems, more doubtfully attributed, include the indifferent "A Lover's Complaint" and the string of songs and poems collected in *The Passionate Pilgrim.* Of these, the poems most clearly Shakespeare's were lifted—some rather carelessly—from the plays and sonnets.

The unfamiliar reader is apt to be the young reader. If you are seventy and have not read Shakespeare, you are young indeed and have much to look forward to. If you are fifteen and *have* read him, you have even more to look forward to, for each new reading increases the delight.

Among the most delightful of Shakespeare's poems are the songs he weaves into his plays. All, or nearly all, must have been put to music, though little of it survives. Naturally enough, the songs are most plentiful in the comedies—so much so that some of these might be called musical comedies, if rather more lyrical than we are accustomed to today. But Shakespeare uses songs, as well, in tragedy and historical drama.

Often they serve as pauses, to underscore a mood by intensifying, sometimes by ridiculing it. At the height of Lear's passion, when he is railing against his ungrateful daughters, the Fool interposes mocking ditties, reminding him that he, Lear, is the more fool. It is a turning of the knife in the wound.

Such effects are lost when the songs are extracted from the plays. Or rather, the songs gain added point or poignance in their proper context. "Tell me where is fancy bred, / Or in the heart or in the head?" asks the song in *The Merchant of Venice*. This is thoroughly charming and delightful, but in the play Portia is trying, through the insistent rhyme and the sudden ringing of a knell, to tip off her suitor Bassanio that he will win her hand by choosing the casket of lead.

Not all the songs are original. Shakespeare introduces snatches of ballads, catches and street-songs. The lovely willow song Desdemona sings in *Othello* is an adaptation of several on the same theme. In her distraction, Desdemona interjects an extraneous line after "Sing all a green willow must be my garland": "Let nobody blame him; his scorn I approve." She breaks off with "Nay, that's not next!" and resumes the song.

From the innocent gaiety of "Under the greenwood tree" in *As You Like It* to the reeling boisterousness of "The master, the swabber, the boatswain and I" in *The Tempest*, Shakespeare evolves a rich profusion of styles and metres to match every occasion. Some have more syncopation than ever came out of Tin Pan Alley, certainly more sophistication.

He is particularly adept at a certain ragging vein that mocks, but does not dismantle, sentiment. It mocks it, you might say, by more than taking it for granted; it "jazzes it up." If the sentiment can pass this vigorous vulgarization, this roughing-up, it emerges as a true sentiment.

And Shakespeare can put this to the most "serious" of uses; as in *Hamlet*, Ophelia's bawdy jingles are the most affecting evidence of her derangement. They are unsurpassed as dramatic presentations of madness. Shakespeare, past master of the most exquisite nuance and of the belly laugh, can manage them both in the one breath.

Two of his favorite subjects for ridicule, particularly in the early comedies, are poetry and love. In *Love's Labour's Lost* the nobility playing at "art-forms" comes in for a ribbing. The sonnet that Ferdinand, King of Navarre, so laboriously composes ("So sweet a kiss the golden sun gives not") is a travesty—a critique by example—of the full-blown style rampant when Shakespeare began writing.

Similarly his approach to love begins in mockery. In another early play, *Two Gentlemen of Verona*, the point of the magically beautiful "Who is Silvia?" is that it has no point. It is arrant nonsense. "What," indeed, "*is* she?"

As portrayed, Silvia may well be "fair," but she is neither "holy" nor "wise." She is just any pretty young girl. Even Proteus, plotting to take her away from her true love (and his best friend) Valentine, cannot explain to himself why he so suddenly prefers her to his own true love, Julia, another pretty young girl. Perhaps, he thinks,

7

it is because Valentine has praised her so inordinately.

Under the guise, or disguise, of wooing her on behalf of still a third suitor, the boorish Thurio, he has her serenaded with this song, which might just as well have asked, "Who is Julia?" In the early comedies, the heroines are all but interchangeable. In *A Midsummer Night's Dream,* Hermia and Helena are differentiated by height, but little else. Katharina in *The Taming of the Shrew* has a more pronounced character, but it is negative, a willfulness that the action of the play is to break, as one would curb a horse. She winds up more compliant than her sister Bianca. Only gradually do Shakespeare's heroines take on dimension, rather than serving as foils for any swain's ideal of perfection.

Some of the songs and incidental poems carry bits of dialogue, like earth around a root. The sonnet Romeo and Juliet alternately say to each other on meeting is followed by a quatrain, in riposte, leading up to the second stolen kiss. The song Pistol and the boy sing during the battle in *King Henry the Fifth* could not be understood without the boy's profound wish to be far away in London. So too, in *A Midsummer Night's Dream,* Nick Bottom's mad lines beginning "The raging rocks" lose even the point of their nonsense if we do not know what part he thinks he is playing.

For this book, I have also selected a few passages not strictly poems in their own right, lyrical interludes that seem set aside from the action or that make reference, if glancingly and often ironically, to an ever-expanding view of poetry.

Shakespeare must be watched closely for his marvelous byplay. In *The Life of King Henry the Fifth* each act is introduced by a scene-shifting prologue of matchless ingenuity. I have included these as poems, with several ulterior motives. One is to show that in Shakespeare, poetry is not "specialized"; it does everything. Nothing is too menial for it. The play may borrow its plot from history or from other writers, but everything else is created by the poet. Besides supplying the characters and their dialogue, he invents the scenery, the direction and what we have now come to call "the production."

And he does all of this by making his audience work for him. We are cajoled into entering his imagination; as we sit in our seats, he beckons us through time and space: across "the narrow seas" from Southampton to Herfleur and back; to Italy; to Denmark; to Greece; to wherever. And all of this with the utmost simplicity.

I wonder how many hundreds of thousands of dollars were spent on the production of *Henry the Fifth* when it was filmed by Laurence Olivier. I happen to think it was a very fine film. And yet the cameras could not keep up with Shakespeare's lines:

> Thus with imagined wing our swift scene flies
> In motion of no less celerity
> Than that of thought.

It's almost as if Shakespeare had foretold the enormous costs and had counselled restraint: "A little touch of Harry in the night."

Shakespeare is seldom obviously arrogant. And yet,

pretending to apologize as he does in these choruses, he cannot resist interjecting a sly, literal plea for the imagination as against the real thing. He is going to take us, he says in the prologue to Act Two, from England to France —a notoriously rough crossing. Very casually he notes: "We'll not offend one stomach with our play."

Even more slyly, in the lines with which Henry woos Katharine of France, Shakespeare proceeds to undermine poetry. Henry speaks "plain soldier"; he has, he says, "neither words nor measure." And yet his unmeasured speech becomes the most moving of love poems. It reaches inspired eloquence in its very rejection of the traditional "poetic" stance of courtship: "if thou canst love me for this, take me; if not, to say to thee that I shall die, is true; but for thy love, by the Lord, no; yet I love thee too."

The most natural transition from Shakespeare's poems to his theatre is *A Midsummer Night's Dream*. I was tempted to include it in full, as a long poem. As the number of songs from it will suggest, it is perhaps the most lyrical of his plays. Others may have richer, more profound poetry; but none, with the possible exception of his late masterpiece *The Tempest*, sustains such a glimmering, shimmering magic. It has been called a distillation of moonlight; certainly it is all compact of "airy nothing."

Edgar Allan Poe has said that there is no such thing as a long poem. He is thinking of a pure lyric effect, which can seldom be extended without tedium. What we would call a long poem, like *Paradise Lost,* he would say was a mixture of poetry and narrative. A verse drama, the blending of poetry and action, is not usually thought of as a poem.

But *A Midsummer Night's Dream* is short. Not in its actual time span, which is the conventional length for a play. But its speed, the fragility of its action, images and ideas, and the way these keep constantly revolving, all contribute to a singular unity of effect. "Are you sure," asks Demetrius, one of the lovers, "That we are awake? It seems to me / That we yet sleep, we dream."

What makes this play a poem is that it is, in essence, a three-way metaphor comparing "the lunatic, the lover and the poet." What they have in common, in the eloquent words with which Duke Theseus opens the Fifth Act, is "strong imagination." The little group of Athenian (but very Cockney) workmen, earnestly rehearsing and then performing their "most Lamentable Comedy and most Cruel Death of Pyramus and Thisby" for the Duke and his bride, would not qualify as certified madmen. But their imagination is quite zany. Unable to bring a wall on the stage, they have one of their number, "Snout by name," enact the role. This he does so persuasively, if not convincingly, that a member of the audience is moved to remark, "It is the wittiest partition that ever I heard discourse."

The middle level is supplied by the courtiers, especially the two pairs of lovers fleeing by night in the nearby woods. Their affections, like a game of musical chairs, keep changing partners. Through them, Shakespeare seems to be poking fun at the extravagant language of much love poetry; it can be applied to anyone. "The lover," says Theseus, "Sees Helen's beauty in a brow of Egypt"—anticipating the Dark Lady of the sonnets, as well as *Antony and Cleopatra.*

"Lord, what fools these mortals be!" says Puck, the mischievous sprite-of-all-chores, who can "put a girdle round about the earth / in forty minutes." He and his master Oberon—indeed, the whole fairy troupe—are pure imagination: "The poet's eye" that "in a fine frenzy rolling / Doth glance from heaven to earth, from earth to heaven."

Yet even the fairies, with their preposterous quarrel and capricious meddling, can be ridiculous. Under the influence of the love-juice their queen, Titania, kisses the "fair large ears" of her new beloved, one of the oafish workmen, on whom Puck has clapped the head of an ass. But if this is the height of absurdity, the enchantment works both ways as, for a bedazzled moment, Nick Bottom the Weaver finds himself the startled lover of the queen.

Throughout, the sublime and the ridiculous are held in solution, bathed in a warm, affectionate and mocking tenderness. A slender situation is reflected and refracted three ways, as in multiple mirrors. And always Shakespeare keeps them one turn ahead of us. We may think he is telling us, in Theseus' much-quoted lines, exactly what he thinks and feels about poetry. But the lines are said by the least "poetic" character in the play, the man of action who, as he tells us, has no belief in any form of imagination whatsoever.

If *A Midsummer Night's Dream* is the most lyrical of Shakespeare's plays, the sonnets are his most dramatic poems. Yet it is a curiously inward drama, at once intensely personal and thoroughly ambiguous. Shakespeare tells all and nothing. The poet who has had Theseus describe the poet as giving "to airy nothing / A local habitation and a name," here gives himself, his friend, his mistress and the rival poet no name and no habitation. They exist in a region of the mind.

True, he does pun on the name "Will," which he seems to share with his friend. And there are enough changes rung on words like "hue," "you," "use," and on "fair," "were," "very" (probably pronounced "vairy" similarly in Elizabethan times) to suggest that the Blond Gentleman of the sonnets might be a member of the Vere (Vair?) family, with the additional name of Hugh or Hughes.

Those who would assign the authorship to Edward de Vere (E. Vere) find their most plausible argument in the poet's unceasing delight in playing on words (probably pronounced something like "vairds"). "Every word doth almost tell my name," says Sonnet 76, which is loaded with "variations" on the sound "vair." An even more romantic notion is that the young man, "the fair friend," is in fact the poet's—and Queen Elizabeth's—secret son.

In any case he is as great a mystery as the Dark Lady and the rival poet. No very clear "story line" emerges from the sonnets, which are quite likely scrambled from the order in which the poet wrote them. He had no hand in their publication.

In the first fifteen, the young man is urged to beget a son; one way of achieving immortality. This theme grows repetitious, almost mechanical, and leads to some of Shakespeare's poorest lines. For he could write poor lines, like the couplet that concludes the twelfth sonnet: "And nothing 'gainst time's scythe can make defence / Save breed to brave him when he takes thee hence."

Gradually the theme alters; the immortality will be conferred by the poet: "And all in war with time for love of you, / As he takes from you, I ingraft you new." (15) This wish recurs with ever-varying inflections: quietly, boastfully, hopefully, doubtfully, pleadingly, despairingly. In the course of developing it, Shakespeare arrives, in Sonnet 81, at his own, unique, dramatist's conception of immortality: "You still shall live—such virtue hath my pen— / Where breath most breathes, even in the mouths of men."

This exhibits the conscious pride of the playwright. He writes lines for other men to say; but he shapes them in such a way that the actor, or the reader, in saying them, must imitate or reproduce his breath. He does not need to sign his name; his breath is his signature; his sonnets are signed, so to speak, on the wind.

This is the inside story of the sonnets. It is also the primary motive of much poetry; seldom has it been expressed quite so intimately, with such subtle simplicity. It is quite literally breath-taking; and the immortality works both ways. When we read a sonnet, we are entitled to feel that we are, for that moment and to the extent that we read it well, reliving Shakespeare.

What we relive in the sonnets is very little biographical

detail; rather we share attitudes toward experience. These attitudes are multiple; sometimes contradictory. Another poet is writing verses to the friend. He is perhaps a better poet. Yet the more artful he is, the poorer poet he is; he lacks Shakespeare's deep sincerity. (A rich vein of irony runs through the sonnets; they are not always to be taken for what they say.) The friend is scolded and forgiven for various unspecified misdemeanors; then very definitely because he has involved himself with the poet's mistress. And then the sonnets return to the friend's "constancy and virtue." It is the poet who has "made myself a motley to the view"—perhaps Shakespeare's estimate of himself as actor-playwright.

But there is no one estimate of anything in Shakespeare, either here or in the plays. He takes every possible view of everything; as Coleridge says, he is "myriad-minded." In the later sonnets to his mistress, he teases her for being an unfashionable brunette, praises her because of it and, in the heat of his anger, bedevils her with it.

But it is the individual sonnets that are dramatic, rather than their cat's-cradle skein. A Shakespearean sonnet is generally a dialogue between ideas or feelings. Its procedure can be as formal as a court of law. Usually one side is given eight lines; the other, four; and the final couplet serves as rebuttal, summation, or resolution. Occasionally, as in Sonnet 42, there is an O. Henry ending, no less surprising for being ironic: "Sweet flattery! then she loves but me alone."

This dialogue form contributes at once to the power and the weakness of Shakespeare's sonnets. Sometimes the resolution seems tacked on, or too easily arrived at; it recedes from the march of thought and music that has led up to it.

But at his lyrical best, as in Sonnet 18 ("Shall I compare thee to a summer's day?"), the conclusion arrives with such effortless serenity that we are only astonished by it afterward:

> So long as men can breathe or eyes can see,
> So long lives this and this gives life to thee.

And at his dramatic best, as in Sonnet 116 ("Let me not to the marriage of true minds / Admit impediments."), it builds architecturally, with all the excitement of a great play building to a resounding curtain line:

> If this be error and upon me proved,
> I never writ, nor no man ever loved.

LLOYD FRANKENBERG

Songs and Poems

from the Plays

My thoughts do harbour with my Silvia nightly
    And slaves they are to me that send them flying:
O! could their master come and go as lightly,
    Himself would lodge where senseless they are lying.
My herald thoughts in thy pure bosom rest them;
    While I, their king, that hither them importune,
Do curse the grace that with such grace hath blessed them,
    Because myself do want my servants' fortune:
I curse myself, for they are sent by me,
That they should harbour where their lord would be.

(Valentine in *The Two Gentlemen of Verona*,
Act Three, Scene One)

Who is Silvia? what is she
   That all our swains commend her?
Holy, fair and wise is she;
   The heavens such grace did lend her
That she might admired be.

Is she kind as she is fair?
   For beauty lives with kindness:
Love doth to her eyes repair
   To help him of his blindness
And, being helped, inhabits there.

Then to Silvia let us sing
   That Silvia is excelling;
She excels each mortal thing
   Upon the dull earth dwelling;
To her let us garlands bring.

(Musicians in *The Two Gentlemen of Verona*,
Act Four, Scene Two)

If she be made of white and red,
    Her faults will ne'er be known;
For blushing cheeks by faults are bred
    And fears by pale white shown:
Then if she fear, or be to blame,
    By this you shall not know,
For still her cheeks possess the same
    Which native she doth owe.

(Moth in *Love's Labour's Lost*,
Act One, Scene Two)

So sweet a kiss the golden sun gives not
To those fresh morning drops upon the rose
As thy eyebeams when their fresh rays have smote
The night of dew that on my cheeks down flows;
Nor shines the silver moon one half so bright
Through the transparent bosom of the deep
As does thy face through tears of mine give light;
Thou shinest in every tear that I do weep:
No drop but as a coach doth carry thee,
So ridest thou triumphing in my woe:
Do but behold the tears that swell in me
And they thy glory through my grief will show:
  But do not love thyself; then thou wilt keep
  My tears for glasses and still make me weep.
  O queen of queens, how far dost thou excel,
  No thought can think nor tongue of mortal tell.

(King Ferdinand in *Love's Labour's Lost*,
Act Four, Scene Three)

On a day, alack the day!
Love, whose month was ever May,
Spied a blossom passing fair
Playing in the wanton air:
Through the velvet leaves the wind
All unseen can passage find,
That the lover, sick to death,
Wished himself the heaven's breath.
Air, quoth he, thy cheeks may blow;
Air, would I might triumph so!
But alack! my hand is sworn
Ne'er to pluck thee from thy thorn:
Vow, alack! for youth unmeet,
Youth so apt to pluck a sweet.
Do not call it sin in me
That I am forsworn for thee;
Thou for whom Jove would swear
Juno but an Ethiop were;
And deny himself for Jove,
Turning mortal for thy love.

(Dumaine in *Love's Labour's Lost*,
Act Four, Scene Three)

Spring

When daisies pied and violets blue
And lady-smocks all silver-white
And cuckoo-buds of yellow hue
Do paint the meadows with delight,
The cuckoo then, on every tree,
Mocks married men; for thus sings he,
      Cuckoo!
Cuckoo, cuckoo: O word of fear,
Unpleasing to a married ear!

When shepherds pipe on oaten straws
And merry larks are ploughmen's clocks,
When turtles tread, and rooks and daws,
And maidens bleach their summer smocks,
The cuckoo then, on every tree,
Mocks married men; for thus sings he,
      Cuckoo!
Cuckoo, cuckoo: O word of fear,
Unpleasing to a married ear!

Winter

When icicles hang by the wall
And Dick the shepherd blows his nail

And Tom bears logs into the hall
And milk comes frozen home in pail,
When blood is nipped and ways be foul,
Then nightly sings the staring owl,
      Tu-who!
To-whit, tu-who: a merry note,
While greasy Joan doth keel the pot.

When all aloud the wind doth blow,
And coughing drowns the parson's saw,
And birds sit brooding in the snow,
And Marian's nose looks red and raw,
When roasted crabs hiss in the bowl,
Then nightly sings the staring owl,
      Tu-who!
To-whit, tu-who: a merry note,
While greasy Joan doth keel the pot.

(Moth, Costard and others in *Love's Labour's Lost*,
Act Five, Scene Two)

Quince	You, Nick Bottom, are set down for Pyramus.
Bottom	What is Pyramus? a lover or a tyrant?
Quince	A lover that kills himself, most gallant, for love.
Bottom	That will ask some tears in the true performing of it. If I do it, let the audience look to their eyes. I will move storms; I will condole in some measure. To the rest. Yet my chief humour is for a tyrant. I could play Ercles rarely, or a part to tear a cat in, to make all split.

> "The raging rocks
> And shivering shocks
> Shall break the locks
>   Of prison gates;
> And Phibbus' car
> Shall shine from far
> And make and mar
>   The foolish Fates."

This was lofty. Now name the rest of the players. This is Ercles' vein, a tyrant's vein. A lover is more condoling.

(*A Midsummer Night's Dream*,
Act One, Scene Two)

Over hill, over dale,
   Thorough bush, thorough brier,
Over park, over pale,
   Thorough flood, thorough fire;
I do wander everywhere,
Swifter than the moon's sphere;
And I serve the Fairy Queen,
To dew her orbs upon the green.
The cowslips tall her pensioners be.
In their gold coats spots you see:
Those be rubies, fairy favours;
In those freckles live their savours.
I must go seek some dewdrops here
And hang a pearl in every cowslip's ear.

(Fairy in *A Midsummer Night's Dream*,
Act Two, Scene One)

I know a bank where the wild thyme blows,
Where oxlips and the nodding violet grows,
Quite over-canopied with luscious woodbine,
With sweet musk-roses and with eglantine.
There sleeps Titania sometime of the night,
Lulled in these flowers with dances and delight;
And there the snake throws her enamelled skin,
Weed wide enough to wrap a fairy in.
And with the juice of this I'll streak her eyes
And make her full of hateful fantasies.

(Oberon in *A Midsummer Night's Dream*,
Act Two, Scene One)

Through the forest have I gone
But Athenian found I none
On whose eyes I might approve
This flower's force in stirring love.
Night and silence! Who is here?
Weeds of Athens he doth wear.
This is he (my master said)
Despisèd the Athenian maid;
And here the maiden, sleeping sound
On the dank and dirty ground.
Pretty soul, she durst not lie
Near this lack-love, this kill-courtesy.
Churl, upon thy eyes I throw
All the power this charm doth owe:
When thou wak'st, let love forbid
Sleep his seat on thy eyelid.
So awake when I am gone,
For I must now to Oberon.

(Puck in *A Midsummer Night's Dream*,
Act Two, Scene Two)

First Fairy You spotted snakes with double tongue,
     Thorny hedgehogs, be not seen;
    Newts and blindworms, do no wrong,
     Come not near our Fairy Queen.

All   Philomele, with melody
    Sing in our sweet lullaby,
    Lulla, lulla, lullaby; lulla, lulla, lullaby;
     Never harm
      Nor spell nor charm
    Come our lovely lady nigh.
    So good night, with lullaby.

First Fairy Weaving spiders, come not here:
     Hence, you long-legged spinners, hence!
    Beetles black, approach not near;
     Worm nor snail, do no offense.

All   Philomele, with melody
    Sing in our sweet lullaby,
    Lulla, lulla, lullaby; lulla, lulla, lullaby;
     Never harm
      Nor spell nor charm
    Come our lovely lady nigh.
    So good night, with lullaby. *She sleeps*

Second Fairy Hence, away! Now all is well.
    One aloof stand sentinel. *Exeunt Fairies*

Enter Oberon and squeezes the flower on Titania's eyelids

Oberon   What thou seest when thou dost wake,
           Do it for thy true-love take;
           Love and languish for his sake.
           Be it ounce or cat or bear,
           Pard or boar with bristled hair
           In thy eye that shall appear
           When thou wak'st, it is thy dear.
           Wake when some vile thing is near.   *Exit*

(*A Midsummer Night's Dream*,
Act Three, Scene One)

Bottom   The woosel cock so black of hue.
            With orange-tawny bill,
        The throstle with his note so true,
            The wren with little quill—

Titania   What angel wakes me from my flowery bed?

Bottom   The finch, the sparrow and the lark,
            The plain-song cuckoo grey,
        Whose note full many a man doth mark
            And dares not answer nay.

        For, indeed, who would set his wit to so foolish a
        bird? Who would give a bird the lie, though he
        cry "cuckoo" never so?

Titania   I pray thee, gentle mortal, sing again.
        Mine ear is much enamored of thy note;
        So is my ear enthrallèd to thy shape;
        And thy fair virtue's force (perforce) doth
            move me
        On the first view, to say, to swear, I love thee.

(*A Midsummer Night's Dream,*
Act Three, Scene One)

Out of this wood do not desire to go.
Thou shalt remain here, whether thou wilt or no.
I am a spirit of no common rate,
The summer still doth tend upon my state;
And I do love thee. Therefore go with me.
I'll give thee fairies to attend on thee
And they shall fetch thee jewels from the deep
And sing while thou on pressèd flowers dost sleep;
And I will purge thy mortal grossness so
That thou shalt like an airy spirit go.

(Titania to Bottom in *A Midsummer Night's Dream*,
Act Three, Scene One)

Oberon   Flower of this purple dye,
                Hit with Cupid's archery,
                Sink in apple of his eye!
                When his love he doth espy,
                Let her shine as gloriously
                As the Venus of the sky.
                When thou wak'st, if she be by,
                Beg of her for remedy.

Puck   Captain of our fairy band,
                Helena is here at hand
                And the youth, mistook by me,
                Pleading for a lover's fee.
                Shall we their fond pageant see?
                Lord, what fools these mortals be!

Oberon   Stand aside. The noise they make
                Will cause Demetrius to awake.

Puck   Then will two at once woo one:
                That must needs be sport alone.
                And those things do best please me
                That befall prepost'rously.

(*A Midsummer Night's Dream*,
Act Three, Scene Two)

Helena O weary night, O long and tedious night,
  Abate thy hours. Shine comforts from the east,
 That I may back to Athens by daylight
  From these that my poor company detest;
 And sleep, that sometimes shuts up sorrow's eye,
 Steal me awhile from mine own company. *Sleeps*

Puck   Yet but three? Come one more.
    Two of both kinds makes up four.
    Here she comes, curst and sad.
    Cupid is a knavish lad
    Thus to make poor females mad.
         Enter Hermia

Hermia Never so weary, never so in woe,
  Bedabbled with the dew and torn with briers,
 I can no further crawl, no further go;
  My legs can keep no pace with my desires.
 Here will I rest me till the break of day.
 Heaven shield Lysander, if they mean a fray!
      Lies down and sleeps

Puck   On the ground
    Sleep sound
    I'll apply
    To your eye,
   Gentle lover, remedy.
    Squeezes the herb on Lysander's eyelids

When thou wak'st
Thou tak'st
True delight
In the sight
Of thy former lady's eye:
And the country proverb known,
That every man should take his own,
In your waking shall be shown:
Jack shall have Jill,
Naught shall go ill,
The man shall have his mare again and all shall
be well.

(*A Midsummer Night's Dream*,
Act Three, Scene Two)

Hippolyta   'Tis strange, my Theseus, that these lovers
             speak of.

Theseus   More strange than true. I never may believe
            These antic fables nor these fairy toys.
            Lovers and madmen have such seething brains,
            Such shaping fantasies that apprehend
            More than cool reason ever comprehends.
            The lunatic, the lover and the poet
            Are of imagination all compact.
            One sees more devils than vast hell can hold:
            That is the madman. The lover, all as frantic,
            Sees Helen's beauty in a brow of Egypt.
            The poet's eye, in a fine frenzy rolling,
            Doth glance from heaven to earth, from earth
              to heaven;
            And as imagination bodies forth
            The forms of things unknown, the poet's pen
            Turns them to shapes and gives to airy nothing
            A local habitation and a name.
            Such tricks hath strong imagination
            That if it would but apprehend some joy,
             It comprehends some bringer of that joy;
            Or in the night imagining some fear,
            How easy is a bush supposed a bear!

(*A Midsummer Night's Dream*,
Act Five, Scene One)

Sweet moon, I thank thee for thy sunny beams;
   I thank thee, moon, for shining now so bright;
For, by thy gracious, golden, glittering gleams,
   I trust to take of truest Thisby sight.

        But stay: O spite!
        But mark, poor knight,
     What dreadful dole is here?
        Eyes, do you see?
        How can it be?
     O dainty duck, O dear!
        Thy mantle good,
        What, stained with blood?
     Approach, ye Furies fell!
        O Fates, come, come,
        Cut thread and thrum,
     Quail, crush, conclude, and quell!

O, wherefore, Nature, didst thou lions frame?
   Since lion vile hath here deflowered my dear;
Which is—no, no!—which was the fairest dame
   That lived, that loved, that liked, that looked with cheer.

        Come tears, confound,
        Out, sword, and wound
     The pap of Pyramus:
        Ay, that left pap

Where heart doth hop. *Stabs himself*
Thus die I, thus, thus, thus.
Now am I dead,
Now am I fled.
My soul is in the sky.
Tongue, lose thy light,
Moon, take thy flight *Exit Moonshine*
Now die, die, die, die, die. *Dies*

(Bottom as Pyramus in *A Midsummer Night's Dream,*
Act Five, Scene One)

Asleep, my love?
What, dead, my dove?
O Pyramus, arise!
Speak, speak. Quite dumb?
Dead, dead? A tomb
Must cover thy sweet eyes.
These lily lips,
This cherry nose,
These yellow cowslip cheeks,
Are gone, are gone.
Lovers, make moan.
His eyes were green as leeks.
O Sisters Three,
Come, come to me,
With hands as pale as milk;
Lay them in gore,
Since you have shore
With shears his thread of silk.
Tongue, not a word.
Come, trusty sword,
Come, blade, my breast imbrue! *Stabs herself*
And farewell, friends.
Thus Thisby ends.
Adieu, adieu, adieu.   *Dies*

(Flute as Thisby in *A Midsummer Night's Dream*
Act Five, Scene One)

Now the hungry lion roars,
    And the wolf behowls the moon;
Whilst the heavy ploughman snores,
    All with weary task fordone.
Now the wasted brands do glow,
    Whilst the screech owl, screeching loud,
Puts the wretch that lies in woe
    In remembrance of a shroud.
Now it is the time of night
    That the graves, all gaping wide,
Every one lets forth his sprite,
    In the churchway paths to glide.
And we fairies, that do run
    By the triple Hecate's team
From the presence of the sun,
    Following darkness like a dream,
Now are frolic. Not a mouse
Shall disturb this hallowed house.
I am sent, with broom, before,
To sweep the dust behind the door.

(Puck in *A Midsummer Night's Dream*,
Act Five, Scene One)

Oberon Through the house give glimmering light
     By the dead and drowsy fire;
    Every elf and fairy sprite
     Hop as light as bird from brier
    And this ditty, after me,
    Sing and dance it trippingly.

Titania First rehearse your song by rote,
    To each word a warbling note.
    Hand in hand, with fairy grace,
    Will we sing and bless this place.

Oberon Now until the break of day
    Through this house each fairy stray.
    To the best bride-bed will we,
    Which by us shall blessèd be
    And the issue there create
    Ever shall be fortunate.
    So shall all the couples three
    Ever true in loving be
    And the blots of Nature's hand
    Shall not in their issue stand.
    Never mole, harelip nor scar
    Nor mark prodigious, such as are
    Despisèd in nativity,
    Shall upon their children be.
    With this field-dew consecrate,

Every fairy take his gait
And each several chamber bless,
Through this palace, with sweet peace,
And the owner of it blest
Ever shall in safety rest.
Trip away; make no stay;
Meet me all by break of day.

(*A Midsummer Night's Dream,*
Act Five, Scene One)

If we shadows have offended,
Think but this and all is mended—
That you have but slumbered here
While these visions did appear
And this weak and idle theme,
No more yielding but a dream.
Gentles, do not reprehend.
If you pardon, we will mend
And, as I am an honest Puck,
If we have unearnèd luck
Now to scape the serpent's tongue,
We will make amends ere long;
Else the Puck a liar call.
So, good night unto you all.
Give me your hands, if we be friends,
And Robin shall restore amends.

(Puck in *A Midsummer Night's Dream*,
Conclusion)

Romeo	If I profane with my unworthiest hand
	This holy shrine, the gentle fine is this:
	My lips, two blushing pilgrims, ready stand
	To smooth that rough touch with a tender kiss.
Juliet	Good pilgrim, you do wrong your hand too much,
	Which mannerly devotion shows in this;
	For saints have hands that pilgrims' hands do touch
	And palm to palm is holy palmers' kiss.
Romeo	Have not saints lips, and holy palmers too?
Juliet	Ay, pilgrim, lips that they must use in prayer.
Romeo	O! then, dear saint, let lips do what hands do;
	They pray: grant thou, lest faith turn to despair.
Juliet	Saints do not move, though grant for prayers' sake.
Romeo	Then move not while my prayer's effect I take.
	Kisses her
	Thus from my lips, by thine, my sin is purged.
Juliet	Then have my lips the sin that they have took.
Romeo	Sin from my lips? O trespass sweetly urged!
	Give me my sin again. *Kisses her again*
Juliet	You kiss by the book.

(*Romeo and Juliet*,
Act One, Scene Five)

Tell me where is fancy bred,
Or in the heart or in the head?
How begot, how nourishèd?
    Reply, reply.
It is engendered in the eyes,
With gazing fed; and fancy dies
In the cradle where it lies.
        Let us all ring fancy's knell:
        I'll begin it,—Ding, dong, bell.
Ding, dong, bell.

(Singers in *The Merchant of Venice*,
Act Three, Scene Two)

How sweet the moonlight sleeps upon this bank!
Here will we sit and let the sounds of music
Creep in our ears; soft stillness and the night
Become the touches of sweet harmony.
Sit, Jessica. Look! how the floor of heaven
Is thick inlaid with patines of bright gold.
There's not the smallest orb, which thou behold'st,
But in his motion like an angel sings,
Still quiring to the young-eyed cherubims;
Such harmony is in immortal souls.
But, whilst this muddy vesture of decay
Doth grossly close it in, we cannot hear it.

(Lorenzo in *The Merchant of Venice*,
Act Five, Scene One)

Do nothing but eat and make good cheer
And praise God for the merry year,
When flesh is cheap and females dear
And lusty lads roam here and there
        So merrily
And ever among so merrily.

Be merry, be merry, my wife has all,
For women are shrews, both short and tall:
'Tis merry in hall, when beards wag all
        And welcome merry Shrovetide.
Be merry, be merry.

A cup of wine that's brisk and fine
And drink unto the leman mine
        And a merry heart lives long-a.

Fill the cup and let it come;
I'll pledge you a mile to the bottom.

Do me right
And dub me knight,
        Samingo!

(Silence in *King Henry IV, Part II*,
Act Five, Scene Three)

Sigh no more, ladies, sigh no more,
    Men were deceivers ever;
One foot in sea and one on shore,
    To one thing constant never.
        Then sigh not so
        But let them go
And be you blithe and bonny,
Converting all your sounds of woe
Into Hey nonny, nonny.

Sing no more ditties, sing no moe
    Of dumps so dull and heavy;
The fraud of men was ever so
    Since summer first was leavy.
        Then sigh not so
        But let them go
And be you blithe and bonny,
Converting all your sounds of woe
Into Hey nonny, nonny.

(Balthazar in *Much Ado About Nothing,*
Act Two, Scene Three)

O! for a muse of fire that would ascend
The brightest heaven of invention;
A kingdom for a stage, princes to act
And monarchs to behold the swelling scene.
Then should the warlike Harry, like himself,
Assume the port of Mars; and at his heels,
Leashed in like hounds, should famine, sword and fire
Crouch for employment. But pardon, gentles all,
The flat unraisèd spirits that have dared
On this unworthy scaffold to bring forth
So great an object: can this cockpit hold
The vasty fields of France? Or may we cram
Within this wooden O the very casques
That did affright the air at Agincourt?
O pardon! since a crooked figure may
Attest in little place a million;
And let us, ciphers to this great accompt,
On your imaginary forces work.
Suppose within the girdle of these walls
Are now confined two mighty monarchies,
Whose high uprearèd and abutting fronts
The perilous narrow ocean parts asunder:
Piece out our imperfections with your thoughts;
Into a thousand parts divide one man
And make imaginary puissance;
Think, when we talk of horses, that you see them
Printing their proud hoofs i' the receiving earth;

For 'tis your thoughts that now must deck our kings,
Carry them here and there, jumping o'er times,
Turning the accomplishment of many years
Into an hour-glass: for the which supply,
Admit me Chorus to this history,
Who prologue-like your humble patience pray,
Gently to hear, kindly to judge our play.

(Chorus in *King Henry V*,
Prologue to Act One)

Now all the youth of England are on fire
And silken dalliance in the wardrobe lies;
Now thrive the armourers, and honour's thought
Reigns solely in the breast of every man:
They sell the pasture now to buy the horse,
Following the mirror of all Christian kings,
With wingèd heels, as English Mercuries.
For now sits expectation in the air
And hides a sword from hilts unto the point
With crowns imperial, crowns and coronets,
Promised to Harry and his followers.
The French, advised by good intelligence
Of this most dreadful preparation,
Shake in their fear, and with pale policy
Seek to divert the English purposes.
O England! model to thy inward greatness,
Like little body with a mighty heart,
What might'st thou do that honour would thee do,
Were all thy children kind and natural!
But see thy fault! France hath in thee found out
A nest of hollow bosoms, which he fills
With treacherous crowns; and three corrupted men—
One, Richard Earl of Cambridge, and the second,
Henry Lord Scroop of Masham, and the third,
Sir Thomas Grey, knight, of Northumberland—
Have, for the gilt of France—O guilt indeed!—
Confirmed conspiracy with fearful France

And by their hands this grace of kings must die,
If hell and treason hold their promises,
Ere he take ship for France, and in Southampton.
Linger your patience on and we'll digest
The abuse of distance as we forge our play.
The sum is paid; the traitors are agreed;
The king is set from London and the scene
Is now transported, gentles, to Southampton:
There is the playhouse now, there must you sit
And thence to France shall we convey you safe
And bring you back, charming the narrow seas
To give you gentle pass; for if we may,
We'll not offend one stomach with our play.
But, till the king come forth, and but till then,
Unto Southampton do we shift our scene.

(Chorus in *King Henry V*,
Prologue to Act Two)

Thus with imagined wing our swift scene flies
In motion of no less celerity
Than that of thought. Suppose that you have seen
The well-appointed king at Hampton pier
Embark his royalty and his brave fleet
With silken streamers the young Phoebus fanning;
Play with your fancies and in them behold
Upon the hempen tackle ship-boys climbing;
Hear the shrill whistle which doth order give
To sounds confused; behold the threaden sails,
Borne with the invisible and creeping wind,
Draw the huge bottoms through the furrowed sea,
Breasting the lofty surge. O! do but think
You stand upon the rivage and behold
A city on the inconstant billows dancing;
For so appears this fleet majestical,
Holding due course to Harfleur. Follow, follow!
Grapple your minds to sternage of this navy
And leave your England, as dead midnight still,
Guardèd with grandsires, babies and old women,
Either past or not arrived to pith and puissance:
For who is he, whose chin is but enriched
With one appearing hair, that will not follow
These culled and choice-drawn cavaliers to France?
Work, work your thoughts and therein see a siege;
Behold the ordnance on their carriages,
With fatal mouths gaping on girded Harfleur.

Suppose the ambassador from the French comes back;
Tells Harry that the king doth offer him
Katharine his daughter and with her, to dowry,
Some petty and unprofitable dukedoms:
The offer likes not: and the nimble gunner
With linstock now the devilish cannon touches,
                    Alarum, and chambers go off
And down goes all before them. Still be kind
And eke out our performance with your mind.

(Chorus in *King Henry V*,
Prologue to Act Three)

Pistol   Knocks go and come; God's vassals drop and die;
   And sword and shield,
    In bloody field,
   Doth win immortal fame.

 Boy   Would I were in an alehouse in London! I would
  give all my fame for a pot of ale and safety.

Pistol   And I:
   If wishes would prevail with me,
   My purpose would not fail with me,
   But thither would I hie.

 Boy   As duly,
   But not as truly,
   As bird doth sing on bough.

(*King Henry V*,
Act Three, Scene Two)

Now entertain conjecture of a time
When creeping murmur and the poring dark
Fills the wide vessel of the universe.
From camp to camp, through the foul womb of night,
The hum of either army stilly sounds,
That the fixed sentinels almost receive
The secret whispers of each other's watch:
Fire answers fire, and through their paly flames
Each battle sees the other's umbered face;
Steed threatens steed, in high and boastful neighs
Piercing the night's dull ear; and from the tents
The armourers, accomplishing the knights,
With busy hammers closing rivets up,
Give dreadful note of preparation.
The country cocks do crow, the clocks do toll
And the third hour of drowsy morning name.
Proud of their numbers and secure in soul,
The confident and over-lusty French
Do the low-rated English play at dice
And chide the cripple tardy-gaited night
Who, like a foul and ugly witch, doth limp
So tediously away. The poor condemnèd English,
Like sacrifices by their watchful fires,
Sit patiently and inly ruminate
The morning's danger, and their gesture sad
Investing lank-lean cheeks and war-worn coats
Presenteth them unto the gazing moon
So many horrid ghosts. O! now, who will behold

The royal captain of this ruined band
Walking from watch to watch, from tent to tent,
Let him cry, "Praise and glory on his head!"
For forth he goes and visits all his host,
Bids them good-morrow with a modest smile
And calls them brothers, friends and countrymen.
Upon his royal face there is no note
How dread an army hath enrounded him;
Nor doth he dedicate one jot of colour
Unto the weary and all-watchèd night;
But freshly looks and overbears attaint
With cheerful semblance and sweet majesty,
That every wretch, pining and pale before,
Beholding him, plucks comfort from his looks.
A largess universal like the sun
His liberal eye doth give to everyone,
Thawing cold fear, that mean and gentle all,
Behold, as may unworthiness define,
A little touch of Harry in the night.
And so our scene must to the battle fly
Where—O! for pity!—we shall much disgrace
With four or five most vile and ragged foils,
Right ill-disposed in brawl ridiculous,
The name of Agincourt. Yet sit and see,
Minding true things by what their mockeries be.

(Chorus in *King Henry V*,
Prologue to Act Four)

Vouchsafe to those that have not read the story
That I may prompt them, and of such as have,
I humbly pray them to admit the excuse
Of time, of numbers and due course of things,
Which cannot in their huge and proper life
Be here presented. Now we bear the king
Toward Calais: grant him there; there seen,
Heave him away upon your wingèd thoughts
Athwart the sea. Behold! the English beach
Pales in the flood with men, with wives and boys,
Whose shouts and claps out-voice the deep-mouthed sea,
Which, like a mighty whiffler, 'fore the king
Seems to prepare his way: so let him land
And solemnly see him set on to London.
So swift a pace hath thought that even now
You may imagine him upon Blackheath,
Where that his lords desire him to have borne
His bruisèd helmet and his bended sword
Before him through the city: he forbids it,
Being free from vainness and self-glorious pride,
Giving full trophy, signal and ostent,
Quite from himself, to God. But now behold,
In the quick forge and working-house of thought,
How London doth pour out her citizens.
The mayor and all his brethren in best sort,
Like to the senators of the antique Rome,
With the plebeians swarming at their heels,
Go forth and fetch their conquering Caesar in:

As, by a lower but loving likelihood,
Were now the general of our gracious empress,
As in good time he may, from Ireland coming,
Bringing rebellion broachèd on his sword,
How many would the peaceful city quit
To welcome him! Much more, and much more cause,
Did they this Harry. Now in London place him,
As yet the lamentation of the French
Invites the King of England's stay at home;
The emperor coming in behalf of France
To order peace between them; and omit
All the occurrences, whatever chanced
Till Harry's back-return again to France:
There must we bring him, and myself have played
The interim by remembering you 'tis past.
Then brook abridgement and your eyes advance
After your thoughts straight back again to France.

(Chorus in *King Henry V*,
Prologue to Act Five)

King Henry   Marry, if you would put me to verses, or
to dance for your sake, Kate, why you un-
did me: for the one, I have neither words
nor measure, and for the other, I have no
strength in measure, yet a reasonable measure of strength. If I could win a lady at
leap-frog, or by vaulting into my saddle
with my armour on my back—under the
correction of bragging be it spoken—I
should quickly leap into a wife. Or if I
might buffet for my love, or bound my
horse for her favours, I could lay on like
a butcher and sit like a jackanapes, never
off. But before God, Kate, I cannot look
greenly nor gasp out my eloquence, nor I
have no cunning in protestation; only down-
right oaths, which I never use till urged,
nor never break for urging. If thou canst
love a fellow of this temper, Kate, whose
face is not worth sun-burning, that never
looks in his glass for love of anything he
sees there, let thine eye be thy cook. I speak
to thee plain soldier: if thou canst love me
for this, take me; if not, to say to thee that
I shall die, is true; but for thy love, by the
Lord, no; yet I love thee too. And while
thou livest, dear Kate, take a fellow of plain

and uncoined constancy, for he perforce must do thee right, because he hath not the gift to woo in other places; for these fellows of infinite tongue, that can rhyme themselves into ladies' favours, they do always reason themselves out again. What! a speaker is but a prater; a rhyme is but a ballad. A good leg will fall, a straight back will stoop, a black beard will turn white, a curled pate will grow bald, a fair face will wither, a full eye will wax hollow; but a good heart, Kate, is the sun and the moon; or rather the sun and not the moon, for it shines bright and never changes, but keeps his course truly. If thou would have such a one, take me; and take me, take a soldier; take a soldier, take a king. And what sayest thou then to my love? speak, my fair, and fairly, I pray thee.

Katharine　　Is it possible dat I should love de enemy of France?

(*King Henry V*,
Act Five, Scene Two)

Fie on sinful fantasy!
Fie on lust and luxury!
Lust is but a bloody fire,
Kindled with unchaste desire,
Fed in heart, whose flames aspire
As thoughts do blow them higher and higher.
Pinch him, fairies, mutually;
Pinch him for his villainy;
Pinch him and burn him and turn him about,
Till candles and starlight and moonshine be out.

(Fairies in *The Merry Wives of Windsor*,
Act Five, Scene Five)

Under the greenwood tree
Who loves to lie with me
And tune his merry note
Unto the sweet bird's throat,
Come hither, come hither, come hither:
     Here shall he see
     No enemy
But winter and rough weather.

Who doth ambition shun
And loves to live i' the sun,
Seeking the food he eats
And pleased with what he gets,
Come hither, come hither, come hither:
     Here shall he see
     No enemy
But winter and rough weather.

(Amiens in *As You Like It*,
Act Two, Scene Five)

If it do come to pass
That any man turn ass,
Leaving his wealth and ease
A stubborn will to please,
Ducdame, ducdame, ducdame;
Here shall he see
Gross fools as he,
An if he will come to me.

(Jaques in *As You Like It*,
Act Two, Scene Five)

Blow, blow, thou winter wind,
Thou art not so unkind
As man's ingratitude;
Thy tooth is not so keen,
Because thou art not seen,
Although thy breath be rude.
Heigh-ho! sing, heigh-ho! unto the green holly:
Most friendship is feigning, most loving mere folly.
Then heigh-ho! the holly! This life is most jolly.

Freeze, freeze, thou bitter sky,
That dost not bite so nigh
As benefits forgot:
Though thou the water warp,
Thy sting is not so sharp
As friend remembered not.
Heigh-ho! sing, heigh-ho! unto the green holly:
Most friendship is feigning, most loving mere folly.
Then heigh-ho! the holly! This life is most jolly.

(Amiens in *As You Like It*,
Act Two, Scene Seven)

Jaques   Which is he that killed the deer?

Lord   Sir, it was I.

Jaques   Let's present him to the Duke, like a Roman conqueror; and it would do well to set the deer's horns upon his head, for a branch of victory. Have you no song, forester, for this purpose?

Forester   Yes, sir.

Jaques   Sing it; 'tis no matter how it be in tune, so it make noise enough.

Song

What shall he have that killed the deer?
Its leather skin and horns to wear.
    Then sing him home.
Take thou no scorn to wear the horn;
It was a crest ere thou wast born;
      Thy father's father wore it,
      And thy father bore it.
The horn, the horn, the lusty horn,
Is not a thing to laugh to scorn.

(Singers in *As You Like It*,
Act Four, Scene One)

It was a lover and his lass,
    With a hey and a ho and a hey nonino,
That o'er the green corn-field did pass
    In the spring time, the only pretty ring time,
When birds do sing, hey ding a ding, ding;
Sweet lovers love the spring.

Between the acres of the rye,
    With a hey and a ho and a hey nonino,
These pretty country folks would lie
    In the spring time, the only pretty ring time,
When birds do sing, hey ding a ding, ding;
Sweet lovers love the spring.

This carol they began that hour,
    With a hey and a ho and a hey nonino,
How that life was but a flower
    In the spring time, the only pretty ring time,
When birds do sing, hey ding a ding, ding;
Sweet lovers love the spring.

And therefore take the present time,
    With a hey and a ho and a hey nonino;
For love is crownèd with the prime
    In the spring time, the only pretty ring time,
When birds do sing, hey ding a ding, ding;
Sweet lovers love the spring.

(Pageboys in *As You Like It,*
Act Five, Scene Three)

If music be the food of love, play on;
Give me excess of it, that, surfeiting,
The appetite may sicken, and so die.
That strain again! it had a dying fall:
O! it came o'er my ear like the sweet sound
That breathes upon a bank of violets,
Stealing and giving odour. Enough! no more:
'Tis not so sweet now as it was before.
O spirit of love! how quick and fresh art thou,
That, notwithstanding thy capacity
Receiveth as the sea, nought enters there,
Of what validity and pitch soe'er,
But falls into abatement and low price,
Even in a minute: so full of shapes is fancy,
That it alone is high fantastical.

(Duke in *Twelfth Night,*
Act One, Scene One)

Viola   If I did love you in my master's flame,
          With such a suffering, such a deadly life,
          In your denial I would find no sense;
          I would not understand it.
Olivia   Why, what would you?
Viola   Make me a willow cabin at your gate
          And call upon my soul within the house;
          Write loyal cantons of contemnèd love
          And sing them loud even in the dead of night;
          Holla your name to the reverberate hills
          And make the babbling gossip of the air
          Cry out, "Olivia!" O! you should not rest
          Between the elements of air and earth,
          But you should pity me.

(*Twelfth Night*,
Act One, Scene Five)

O mistress mine! where are you roaming?
O stay and hear; your true love's coming
   That can sing both high and low.
Trip no further, pretty sweeting;
Journeys end in lovers meeting,
   Every wise man's son doth know.

What is love? 'tis not hereafter;
Present mirth hath present laughter;
   What's to come is still unsure:
In delay there lies no plenty;
Then come kiss me, sweet and twenty,
   Youth's a stuff will not endure.

(Clown in *Twelfth Night*,
Act Two, Scene Three)

Come away, come away, death,
   And in sad cypress let me be laid;
Fly away, fly away, breath,
   I am slain by a fair cruel maid.
My shroud of white, stuck all with yew,
   O! prepare it.
My part of death, no one so true
   Did share it.

Not a flower, not a flower sweet
   On my black coffin let there be strown;
Not a friend, not a friend greet
   My poor corpse, where my bones shall be thrown.
A thousand thousand sighs to save,
   Lay me, O! where
Sad true lover never find my grave,
   To weep there.

(Clown in *Twelfth Night*,
Act Two, Scene Four)

I am gone, sir,
And anon, sir,
I'll be with you again,
In a trice,
Like to the old Vice,
Your need to sustain;

Who with dagger of lath,
In his rage and his wrath,
Cries Ah ha! to the divel:
Like a mad lad,
Pare thy nails, dad;
Adieu, goodman divel.

(Clown to Malvolio in *Twelfth Night*,
Act Four, Scene Two)

When that I was and a little tiny boy,
   With hey, ho, the wind and the rain,
A foolish thing was but a toy,
   For the rain it raineth every day.

But when I came to man's estate,
   With hey, ho, the wind and the rain,
'Gainst knaves and thieves men shut their gate,
   For the rain it raineth every day.

But when I came, alas, to wive,
   With hey, ho, the wind and the rain,
By swaggering could I never thrive,
   For the rain it raineth every day.

But when I came unto my beds,
   With hey, ho, the wind and the rain,
With toss-pots still had drunken heads,
   For the rain it raineth every day.

A great while ago the world begun,
   With hey, ho, the wind and the rain,
But that's all one, our play is done,
   And we'll strive to please you every day.

(Clown in *Twelfth Night*,
Act Five, Scene One)

How should I your true love know
  From another one?
By his cockle hat and staff
  And his sandal shoon.

He is dead and gone, lady,
  He is dead and gone;
At his head a grass-green turf,
  At his heels a stone.

White his shroud as the mountain snow,
  Larded with sweet flowers;
Which bewept to the grave did go
  With true-love showers.

(Ophelia in *Hamlet*,
Act Four, Scene Five)

Tomorrow is Saint Valentine's day,
   All in the morning betime,
And I a maid at your window,
   To be your Valentine.

Then up he rose and donned his clothes
   And dupped the chamber-door;
Let in the maid that out a maid
   Never departed more.

By Gis and by Saint Charity,
   Alack and fie for shame!
Young men will do 't, if they come to 't;
   By cock, they are to blame.

Quoth she, before you tumbled me,
   You promised me to wed.
So would I ha' done, by yonder sun,
   And thou hadst not come to my bed.

(Ophelia in *Hamlet*,
Act Four, Scene Five)

And will he not come again?
And will he not come again?
    No, no, he is dead,
    Go to thy death-bed,
He never will come again.

His beard was as white as snow
All flaxen was his poll:
    He is gone, he is gone
    And we cast away moan:
God a mercy on his soul!

(Ophelia in *Hamlet*,
Act Four, Scene Five)

In youth when I did love, did love,
  Methought it was very sweet
To contract, *Oh!* the time for, *Ah!* my behove,
  O methought there was nothing meet.

But age with his stealing steps
  Hath clawed me in his clutch
And hath shipped me intil the land
  As if I had never been such.

A pick-axe and a spade, a spade,
  For and a shrouding sheet:
O a pit of clay for to be made
  For such a guest is meet.

(First Gravedigger in *Hamlet*,
Act Five, Scene One)

Take, O take those lips away,
    That so sweetly were forsworn;
And those eyes, the break of day,
    Lights that do mislead the morn:
But my kisses bring again,
        Bring again,
Seals of love, but sealed in vain,
        Sealed in vain.

(Boy in *Measure for Measure*,
Act Four, Scene One)

And let me the canakin clink, clink
And let me the canakin clink:
   A soldier's a man,
   O! man's life but a span,
Why then, let a soldier drink.

(Iago in *Othello*,
Act Two, Scene Three)

The poor soul sat sighing by a sycamore tree,
    Sing all a green willow;
Her hand on her bosom, her head on her knee,
    Sing willow, willow, willow:

The fresh streams ran by her and murmured her moans;
    Sing willow, willow, willow:
Her salt tears fell from her and softened the stones;
    Sing willow, willow, willow;
    Sing all a green willow must be my garland.

I called my love false love; but what said he then?
    Sing willow, willow, willow:
If I court more women, you'll couch with more men.

(Desdemona in *Othello*,
Act Four, Scene Three)

That lord that counselled thee
    To give away thy land,
Come place him here by me,
    Do thou for him stand:
The sweet and bitter fool
    Will presently appear;
The one in motley here,
    The other found out there.

(Fool in *King Lear*,
Act One, Scene Four)

That sir which serves and seeks for gain
 And follows but for form
Will pack when it begins to rain
 And leave thee in the storm.
But I will tarry; the fool will stay
 And let the wise man fly.
The knave turns fool that runs away;
 The fool no knave, perdy.

(Fool in *King Lear*,
Act Two, Scene Four)

Be thy mouth or black or white,
Tooth that poisons if it bite,
Mastiff, greyhound, mongrel grim,
Hound or spaniel, brach or lym
Or bobtail tike or trundle-tail,
Tom will make them weep and wail:
For, with throwing thus my head,
Dogs leap the hatch and all are fled.

(Edgar in *King Lear*,
Act Three, Scene Six)

First Witch   Thrice the brinded cat hath mewed.

Second Witch   Thrice and once the hedge-pig whined.

Third Witch   Harpier cries: 'Tis time! 'tis time!

First Witch   Round about the cauldron go;
In the poisoned entrails throw:
Toad that under cold stone
Days and nights has thirty-one
Sweltered venom sleeping got,
Boil thou first i' the charmèd pot.

All   Double, double toil and trouble!
Fire burn and cauldron bubble!

Second Witch   Filet of a fenny snake
In the cauldron boil and bake;
Eye of newt and toe of frog,
Wool of bat and tongue of dog,
Adder's fork and blind-worm's sting,
Lizard's leg and howlet's wing,
For a charm of powerful trouble,
Like a hell-broth boil and bubble.

All   Double, double toil and trouble!
Fire burn and cauldron bubble.

Third Witch   Scale of dragon, tooth of wolf,
Witches' mummy, maw and gulf
Of the ravined salt-sea shark,
Root of hemlock digged i' the dark,

Liver of blaspheming Jew,
Gall of goat and slips of yew
Slivered in the moon's eclipse,
Nose of Turk and Tartar's lips,
Finger of birth-strangled babe
Ditch-delivered by a drab;
Add thereto a tiger's chaudron
For the ingredients of our cauldron.

All   Double, double toil and trouble!
Fire burn and cauldron bubble.

Second Witch   Cool it with a baboon's blood,
Then the charm is firm and good.

                    Enter Hecate

Hecate   O! well done! I commend your pains
And everyone shall share i' the gains.
And now about the cauldron sing,
Like elves and fairies in a ring
Enchanting all that you put in.

Music and a song: "Black Spirits," etc.

Second Witch   By the pricking of my thumbs
Something wicked this way comes.
            Open, locks,
            Whoever knocks.

(*Macbeth*,
Act Four, Scene One)

Immortal gods, I crave no pelf;
I pray for no man but myself:
Grant I may never prove so fond
To trust man on his oath or bond,
Or a harlot for her weeping,
Or a dog that seems a-sleeping,
Or a keeper with my freedom,
Or my friends, if I should need 'em.
Amen. So fall to't:
Rich men sin and I eat root.

(Apemantus in *Timon of Athens*,
Act One, Scene Two)

Hark, hark! the lark at heaven's gate sings
　　And Phœbus 'gins arise,
His steeds to water at those springs
　　On chaliced flowers that lies;
And winking Mary-buds begin
　　To ope their golden eyes:
With every thing that pretty is,
　　My lady sweet, arise:
　　　　Arise, arise!

(Musicians in *Cymbeline,*
Act Two, Scene Three)

Fear no more the heat o' the sun
    Nor the furious winter's rages;
Thou thy worldly task hast done,
    Home art gone and ta'en thy wages:
Golden lads and girls all must,
As chimney-sweepers, come to dust.

Fear no more the frown o' the great,
    Thou art past the tyrant's stroke;
Care no more to clothe and eat,
    To thee the reed is as the oak:
The sceptre, learning, physic, must
All follow this and come to dust.

Fear no more the lightning-flash
    Nor the all-dreaded thunder-stone;
Fear not slander, censure rash;
    Thou hast finished joy and moan:
All lovers young, all lovers must
Consign to thee and come to dust.

No exorciser harm thee!
    Nor no witchcraft charm thee!
Ghost unlaid forbear thee!
    Nothing ill come near thee!
Quiet consummation have
And renownèd be thy grave!

(Guiderius and Arviragus in *Cymbeline*,
Act Four, Scene Two)

When daffodils begin to peer,
With heigh! the doxy over the dale,
Why, then comes in the sweet o' the year;
For the red blood reigns in the winter's pale.

The white sheet bleaching on the hedge,
With heigh! the sweet birds, O, how they sing!
Doth set my pugging tooth an edge;
For a quart of ale is a dish for a king.

The lark that tirra-lyra chants,
With heigh! with heigh! the thrush and the jay,
Are summer songs for me and my aunts,
While we lie tumbling in the hay.

(Autolycus in *The Winter's Tale*,
Act Four, Scene Three)

Lawn as white as driven snow;
Cypress black as e'er was crow;
Gloves as sweet as damask roses;
Masks for faces and for noses;
Bugle bracelet, necklace amber,
Perfume for a lady's chamber;
Golden quoifs and stomachers,
For my lads to give their dears;
Pins and poking-sticks of steel;
What maids lack from head to heel:
Come buy of me, come; come buy, come buy!
Buy, lads, or else your lasses cry:
Come buy.

(Autolycus in *The Winter's Tale,*
Act Four, Scene Four)

Come unto these yellow sands
    And then take hands;
Curtsied when you have and kissed
    The wild waves whist,
Foot it featly here and there
And, sweet sprites, bear
The burthen: Hark! hark!
        Bow-wow.
    The watch-dogs bark:
        Bow-wow.
        Hark! hark! I hear
    The strain of strutting Chanticleer
        Cry cock-a-diddle-dow.

(Ariel and Chorus in *The Tempest*,
Act One, Scene Two)

Full fathom five thy father lies:
　　Of his bones are coral made:
Those are pearls that were his eyes;
　　Nothing of him that doth fade
But doth suffer a sea-change
Into something rich and strange.
Sea-nymphs hourly ring his knell:
　　Ding-dong.
Hark! now I hear them—ding-dong bell.

(Ariel in *The Tempest*,
Act One, Scene Two)

The master, the swabber, the boatswain and I,
    The gunner and his mate,
Loved Mall, Meg and Marian and Margery,
    But none of us cared for Kate.
    For she had a tongue with a tang,
    Would cry to a sailor, "Go hang!"
She loved not the savour of tar nor of pitch
Yet a tailor might scratch her where'er she did itch:
    Then to sea, boys, and let her go hang.

(Stephano in *The Tempest,*
Act Two, Scene Two)

No more dams I'll make for fish;
   Nor fetch in firing
   At requiring;
Nor scrape trenchering, nor wash dish:
   'Ban, 'Ban, Ca-caliban
Has a new master: get a new man.

(Caliban in *The Tempest*,
Act Two, Scene Two)

Honour, riches, marriage, blessing,
Long continuance and increasing,
Hourly joys be still upon you!
Juno sings her blessings on you.
Earth's increase and foison plenty,
Barns and garners never empty;
Vines with clustering bunches growing;
Plants with goodly burden bowing;
Spring come to you, at the farthest,
In the very end of harvest!
Scarcity and want shall shun you
Ceres' blessing so is on you.

(Juno and Ceres in *The Tempest*,
Act Four, Scene One)

Where the bee sucks, there suck I;
In a cowslip's bell I lie;
There I couch when owls do cry.
On the bat's back I do fly
After summer merrily.
Merrily, merrily shall I live now
Under the blossom that hangs on the bough.

(Ariel in *The Tempest*,
Act Five, Scene One)

Sonnets

From fairest creatures we desire increase,
That thereby beauty's rose might never die,
But as the riper should by time decease,
His tender heir might bear his memory.
But thou, contracted to thine own bright eyes,
Feed'st thy light's flame with self-substantial fuel,
Making a famine where abundance lies,
Thyself thy foe, to thy sweet self too cruel.
Thou that art now the world's fresh ornament
And only herald to the gaudy spring,
Within thine own bud buriest thy content
And, tender churl, mak'st waste in niggarding.
   Pity the world, or else this glutton be,
    To eat the world's due, by the grave and thee.

Music to hear, why hearest thou music sadly?
Sweets with sweets war not, joy delights in joy.
Why lovest thou that which thou receivest not gladly,
Or else receivest with pleasure thine annoy?
If the true concord of well-tunèd sounds,
By unions married, do offend thine ear,
They do but sweetly chide thee, who confounds
In singleness the parts that thou shouldst bear.
Mark how one string, sweet husband to another,
Strikes each in each by mutual ordering;
Resembling sire and child and happy mother
Who, all in one, one pleasing note do sing;
 Whose speechless song, being many, seeming one,
 Sings this to thee, thou single wilt prove none.

When I consider everything that grows
Holds in perfection but a little moment,
That this huge stage presenteth naught but shows
Whereon the stars in secret influence comment;
When I perceive that men as plants increase,
Cheerèd and checked even by the self-same sky,
Vaunt in their youthful sap, at height decrease,
And wear their brave state out of memory;
Then the conceit of this inconstant stay
Sets you most rich in youth before my sight,
Where wasteful time debateth with decay,
To change your day of youth to sullied night;
   And all in war with time for love of you,
   As he takes from you, I engraft you new.

But wherefore do not you a mightier way
Make war upon this bloody tyrant time
And fortify yourself in your decay
With means more blessèd than my barren rhyme?
Now stand you on the top of happy hours,
And many maiden gardens, yet unset,
With virtuous wish would bear your living flowers,
Much liker than your painted counterfeit.
So should the lines of life that life repair,
Which this time's pencil or my pupil pen,
Neither in inward worth nor outward fair,
Can make you live yourself in eyes of men.
   To give away yourself, keeps yourself still,
   And you must live, drawn by your own sweet skill.

Who will believe my verse in time to come
If it were filled with your most high deserts?
Though yet heaven knows it is but as a tomb
Which hides your life and shows not half your parts.
If I could write the beauty of your eyes
And in fresh numbers number all your graces,
The age to come would say this poet lies,
Such heavenly touches ne'er touched earthly faces.
So should my papers, yellowed with their age,
Be scorned, like old men of less truth than tongue,
And your true rights be termed a poet's rage
And stretchèd metre of an antique song:
    But were some child of yours alive that time,
    You should live twice, in it and in my rhyme.

Shall I compare thee to a summer's day?
Thou art more lovely and more temperate.
Rough winds do shake the darling buds of May
And summer's lease hath all too short a date.
Sometime too hot the eye of heaven shines
And often is his gold complexion dimmed;
And every fair from fair sometime declines,
By chance, or nature's changing course, untrimmed;
But thy eternal summer shall not fade
Nor lose possession of that fair thou owest,
Nor shall death brag thou wanderest in his shade
When in eternal lines to time thou growest.
　So long as men can breathe or eyes can see,
　So long lives this and this gives life to thee.

Devouring Time, blunt thou the lion's paws
And make the earth devour her own sweet brood;
Pluck the keen teeth from the fierce tiger's jaws
And burn the long-lived phoenix in her blood;
Make glad and sorry seasons as thou fleets
And do whate'er thou wilt, swift-footed Time,
To the wide world and all her fading sweets;
But I forbid thee one most heinous crime:
O carve not with thy hours my love's fair brow
Nor draw no lines there with thine antique pen.
Him in thy course untainted do allow
For beauty's pattern to succeeding men.
    Yet do thy worst, old Time; despite thy wrong,
    My love shall in my verse ever live young.

So is it not with me as with that muse,
Stirred by a painted beauty to his verse,
Who heaven itself for ornament doth use
And every fair with his fair doth rehearse,
Making a couplement of proud compare
With sun and moon, with earth and sea's rich gems,
With April's first-born flowers and all things rare
That heaven's air in this huge rondure hems.
O let me, true in love, but truly write,
And then believe me, my love is as fair
As any mother's child, though not so bright
As those gold candles fixed in heaven's air.
　　Let them say more that like of hearsay well;
　　I will not praise that purpose not to sell.

As an unperfect actor on the stage,
Who with his fear is put besides his part,
Or some fierce thing replete with too much rage,
Whose strength's abundance weakens his own heart;
So I, for fear of trust, forget to say
The perfect ceremony of love's rite
And in mine own love's strength seem to decay,
O'ercharged with burthen of mine own love's might.
O let my books be then the eloquence
And dumb presagers of my speaking breast,
Who plead for love and look for recompense
More than that tongue that more hath more expressed.
    O learn to read what silent love hath writ:
    To hear with eyes belongs to love's fine wit.

When in disgrace with fortune and men's eyes,
I all alone beweep my outcast state
And trouble deaf heaven with my bootless cries
And look upon myself and curse my fate,
Wishing me like to one more rich in hope,
Featured like him, like him with friends possessed,
Desiring this man's art and that man's scope,
With what I most enjoy contented least;
Yet in these thoughts myself almost despising,
Haply I think on thee and then my state,
Like to the lark at break of day arising
From sullen earth, sings hymns at heaven's gate;
    For thy sweet love remembered such wealth brings
    That then I scorn to change my state with kings.

When to the sessions of sweet silent thought
I summon up remembrance of things past,
I sigh the lack of many a thing I sought
And with old woes new wail my dear time's waste.
Then can I drown an eye, unused to flow,
For precious friends hid in death's dateless night
And weep afresh love's long since cancelled woe,
And moan th' expense of many a vanished sight.
Then can I grieve at grievances foregone
And heavily from woe to woe tell o'er
The sad account of fore-bemoanèd moan,
Which I new pay as if not paid before.
　　But if the while I think on thee, dear friend,
　　All losses are restored and sorrows end.

Thy bosom is endearèd with all hearts,
Which I by lacking have supposèd dead;
And there reigns love and all love's loving parts
And all those friends which I thought burièd.
How many a holy and obsequious tear
Hath dear religious love stolen from mine eye,
As interest of the dead, which now appear
But things removed that hidden in thee lie.
Thou art the grave where buried love doth live,
Hung with the trophies of my lovers gone,
Who all their parts of me to thee did give;
That due of many now is thine alone.
   Their images I loved I view in thee
   And thou, all they, hast all the all of me.

If thou survive my well-contented day,
When that churl death my bones with dust shall cover,
And shalt by fortune once more re-survey
These poor rude lines of thy deceasèd lover;
Compare them with the bettering of the time
And though they be outstripped by every pen,
Reserve them for my love, not for their rhyme,
Exceeded by the height of happier men.
O then vouchsafe me but this loving thought:
Had my friend's muse grown with this growing age,
A dearer birth than this his love had brought,
To march in ranks of better equipage.
   But since he died and poets better prove,
     Theirs for their style I'll read, his for his love.

Full many a glorious morning have I seen
Flatter the mountain tops with sovereign eye,
Kissing with golden face the meadows green,
Gilding pale streams with heavenly alchemy;
Anon permit the basest clouds to ride
With ugly rack on his celestial face
And from the forlorn world his visage hide,
Stealing unseen to west with this disgrace.
Even so my sun one early morn did shine,
With all triumphant splendour on my brow;
But out alack, he was but one hour mine,
The region cloud hath masked him from me now.
    Yet him for this my love no whit disdaineth;
    Suns of the world may stain when heaven's sun staineth.

No more be grieved at that which thou hast done:
Roses have thorns, and silver fountains mud;
Clouds and eclipses stain both moon and sun,
And loathsome canker lives in sweetest bud.
All men make faults, and even I in this,
Authorizing thy trespass with compare,
Myself corrupting, salving thy amiss,
Excusing thy sins more than their sins are;
For to thy sensual fault I bring in sense—
Thy adverse party is thy advocate—
And 'gainst myself a lawful plea commence.
Such civil war is in my love and hate,
    That I an accessary needs must be
    To that sweet thief which sourly robs from me.

Let me confess that we two must be twain,
Although our undivided loves are one.
So shall those blots that do with me remain,
Without thy help, by me be borne alone.
In our two loves there is but one respect,
Though in our lives a separable spite,
Which though it alter not love's sole effect,
Yet doth it steal sweet hours from love's delight.
I may not evermore acknowledge thee,
Lest my bewailèd guilt should do thee shame;
Nor thou with public kindness honour me,
Unless thou take that honour from thy name.
　　But do not so; I love thee in such sort
　　As thou being mine, mine is thy good report.

How can my muse want subject to invent
While thou dost breathe, that pourest into my verse
Thine own sweet argument, too excellent
For every vulgar paper to rehearse?
O give thyself the thanks, if aught in me
Worthy perusal stand against thy sight;
For who's so dumb that cannot write to thee,
When thou thyself dost give invention light?
Be thou the tenth muse, ten times more in worth
Than those old nine which rhymers invocate;
And he that calls on thee, let him bring forth
Eternal numbers to outlive long date.
    If my slight muse do please these curious days,
    The pain be mine, but thine shall be the praise.

Take all my loves, my love, yea take them all;
What hast thou then more than thou hadst before?
No love, my love, that thou mayst true love call;
All mine was thine, before thou hadst this more.
Then if for my love thou my love receivest,
I cannot blame thee for my love thou usest;
But yet be blamed, if thou this self deceivest
By wilful taste of what thyself refusest.
I do forgive thy robbery, gentle thief,
Although thou steal thee all my poverty;
And yet love knows it is a greater grief
To bear love's wrong than hate's known injury.
     Lascivious grace, in whom all ill well shows,
     Kill me with spites; yet we must not be foes.

Those pretty wrongs that liberty commits
When I am sometime absent from thy heart,
Thy beauty and thy years full well befits,
For still temptation follows where thou art.
Gentle thou art, and therefore to be won;
Beauteous thou art, therefore to be assailed;
And when a woman woos, what woman's son
Will sourly leave her till she have prevailed?
Ay me, but yet thou might'st my seat forbear
And chide thy beauty and thy straying youth,
Who lead thee in their riot even there
Where thou art forced to break a twofold truth:
   Hers, by thy beauty tempting her to thee;
   Thine, by thy beauty being false to me.

That thou hast her, it is not all my grief,
And yet it may be said I loved her dearly;
That she hath thee is of my wailing chief,
A loss in love that touches me more nearly.
Loving offenders, thus I will excuse ye:
Thou dost love her because thou know'st I love her,
And for my sake even so doth she abuse me,
Suffering my friend for my sake to approve her.
If I lose thee, my loss is my love's gain,
And losing her, my friend hath found that loss;
Both find each other and I lose both twain
And both for my sake lay on me this cross.
    But here's the joy: my friend and I are one;
    Sweet flattery! then she loves but me alone.

Not marble nor the gilded monuments
Of princes shall outlive this powerful rhyme;
But you shall shine more bright in these contents
Than unswept stone, besmeared with sluttish time.
When wasteful war shall statues overturn
And broils root out the work of masonry,
Nor Mars his sword nor war's quick fire shall burn
The living record of your memory.
'Gainst death and all-oblivious enmity
Shall you pace forth; your praise shall still find room
Even in the eyes of all posterity
That wear this world out to the ending doom.
So, till the judgement that yourself arise,
You live in this and dwell in lovers' eyes.

Like as the waves make towards the pebbled shore,
So do our minutes hasten to their end;
Each changing place with that which goes before,
In sequent toil all forwards do contend.
Nativity, once in the main of light,
Crawls to maturity, wherewith being crowned,
Crooked eclipses 'gainst his glory fight
And time that gave doth now his gift confound.
Time doth transfix the flourish set on youth
And delves the parallels in beauty's brow,
Feeds on the rarities of nature's truth,
And nothing stands but for his scythe to mow.
    And yet to times in hope my verse shall stand,
    Praising thy worth, despite his cruel hand.

When I have seen by time's fell hand defaced
The rich proud cost of outworn buried age,
When sometime lofty towers I see down-razed,
And brass eternal slave to mortal rage;
When I have seen the hungry ocean gain
Advantage on the kingdom of the shore
And the firm soil win of the watery main,
Increasing store with loss and loss with store;
When I have seen such interchange of state,
Or state itself confounded to decay,
Ruin hath taught me thus to ruminate,
That time will come and take my love away.
   This thought is as a death, which cannot choose
   But weep to have that which it fears to lose.

Since brass, nor stone, nor earth, nor boundless sea,
But sad mortality o'ersways their power,
How with this rage shall beauty hold a plea,
Whose action is no stronger than a flower?
O how shall summer's honey breath hold out
Against the wrackful siege of battering days,
When rocks impregnable are not so stout,
Nor gates of steel so strong but time decays?
O fearful meditation! where, alack,
Shall time's best jewel from time's chest lie hid?
Or what strong hand can hold his swift foot back,
Or who his spoil of beauty can forbid?
    O none, unless this miracle have might,
    That in black ink my love may still shine bright.

No longer mourn for me when I am dead
Than you shall hear the surly sullen bell
Give warning to the world that I am fled
From this vile world with vilest worms to dwell.
Nay, if you read this line, remember not
The hand that writ it, for I love you so
That I in your sweet thought would be forgot
If thinking on me then should make you woe.
O if, I say, you look upon this verse
When I, perhaps, compounded am with clay,
Do not so much as my poor name rehearse
But let your love even with my life decay,
    Lest the wise world should look into your moan
    And mock you with me after I am gone.

That time of year thou mayst in me behold
When yellow leaves, or none, or few, do hang
Upon those boughs which shake against the cold,
Bare ruined choirs, where late the sweet birds sang.
In me thou seest the twilight of such day
As after sunset fadeth in the west,
Which by and by black night doth take away,
Death's second self, that seals up all in rest.
In me thou seest the glowing of such fire,
That on the ashes of his youth doth lie,
As the death-bed whereon it must expire,
Consumed with that which it was nourished by.
   This thou perceiv'st, which makes thy love more strong,
   To love that well which thou must leave ere long.

Why is my verse so barren of new pride,
So far from variation or quick change?
Why with the time do I not glance aside
To new-found methods and to compounds strange?
Why write I still all one, ever the same,
And keep invention in a noted weed,
That every word doth almost tell my name,
Showing their birth and where they did proceed?
O know, sweet love, I always write of you,
And you and love are still my argument.
So all my best is dressing old words new,
Spending again what is already spent;
   For as the sun is daily new and old,
   So is my love still telling what is told.

Whilst I alone did call upon thy aid,
My verse alone had all thy gentle grace;
But now my gracious numbers are decayed
And my sick muse doth give another place.
I grant, sweet love, thy lovely argument
Deserves the travail of a worthier pen,
Yet what of thee thy poet doth invent
He robs thee of and pays it thee again.
He lends thee virtue and he stole that word
From thy behaviour; beauty doth he give
And found it in thy cheek; he can afford
No praise to thee but what in thee doth live.
    Then thank him not for that which he doth say,
    Since what he owes thee thou thyself dost pay.

O how I faint when I of you do write,
Knowing a better spirit doth use your name
And in the praise thereof spends all his might
To make me tongue-tied speaking of your fame.
But since your worth, wide as the ocean is,
The humble as the proudest sail doth bear,
My saucy bark, inferior far to his,
On your broad main doth wilfully appear.
Your shallowest help will hold me up afloat,
Whilst he upon your soundless deep doth ride;
Or, being wracked, I am a worthless boat,
He of tall building and of goodly pride.
    Then if he thrive and I be cast away,
     The worst was this: my love was my decay.

Or I shall live your epitaph to make,
Or you survive when I in earth am rotten,
From hence your memory death cannot take
Although in me each part will be forgotten.
Your name from hence immortal life shall have
Though I, once gone, to all the world must die.
The earth can yield me but a common grave
When you entombèd in men's eyes shall lie.
Your monument shall be my gentle verse
Which eyes not yet created shall o'er-read
And tongues to be your being shall rehearse
When all the breathers of this world are dead.
     You still shall live—such virtue hath my pen—
     Where breath most breathes, even in the mouths of men.

I grant thou wert not married to my muse
And therefore mayst without attaint o'erlook
The dedicated words which writers use
Of their fair subject, blessing every book.
Thou art as fair in knowledge as in hue,
Finding thy worth a limit past my praise;
And therefore art enforced to seek anew
Some fresher stamp of the time-bettering days.
And do so, love; yet when they have devised
What strainèd touches rhetoric can lend,
Thou truly fair, wert truly sympathized
In true plain words by thy true-telling friend;
    And their gross painting might be better used,
    Where cheeks need blood; in thee it is abused.

I never saw that you did painting need
And therefore to your fair no painting set;
I found, or thought I found, you did exceed
The barren tender of a poet's debt:
And therefore have I slept in your report,
That you yourself, being extant, well might show
How far a modern quill doth come too short,
Speaking of worth, what worth in you doth grow.
This silence for my sin you did impute,
Which shall be most my glory, being dumb;
For I impair not beauty, being mute,
When others would give life and bring a tomb.
   There lives more life in one of your fair eyes
   Than both your poets can in praise devise.

Who is it that says most, which can say more
Than this rich praise, that you alone are you,
In whose confine immurèd is the store
Which should example where your equal grew?
Lean penury within that pen doth dwell,
That to his subject lends not some small glory,
But he that writes of you, if he can tell
That you are you, so dignifies his story.
Let him but copy what in you is writ,
Not making worse what nature made so clear,
And such a counterpart shall fame his wit,
Making his style admirèd everywhere.
    You to your beauteous blessings add a curse,
    Being fond on praise, which makes your praises worse.

Was it the proud full sail of his great verse,
Bound for the prize of all too precious you,
That did my ripe thoughts in my brain inhearse,
Making their tomb the womb wherein they grew?
Was it his spirit, by spirits taught to write
Above a mortal pitch, that struck me dead?
No, neither he nor his compeers by night
Giving him aid, my verse astonishèd.
He nor that affable familiar ghost
Which nightly gulls him with intelligence,
As victors, of my silence cannot boast;
I was not sick of any fear from thence.
  But when your countenance filled up his line,
  Then lacked I matter; that enfeebled mine.

Farewell, thou art too dear for my possessing
And like enough thou know'st thy estimate.
The charter of thy worth gives thee releasing;
My bonds in thee are all determinate.
For how do I hold thee but by thy granting
And for that riches where is my deserving?
The cause of this fair gift in me is wanting
And so my patent back again is swerving.
Thyself thou gav'st, thy own worth then not knowing
Or me, to whom thou gav'st it, else mistaking;
So thy great gift, upon misprision growing,
Comes home again, on better judgment making.
   Thus have I had thee as a dream doth flatter:
   In sleep a king, but waking no such matter.

Then hate me when thou wilt; if ever, now;
Now while the world is bent my deeds to cross,
Join with the spite of fortune, make me bow
And do not drop in for an after-loss.
Ah do not, when my heart hath 'scaped this sorrow,
Come in the rearward of a conquered woe;
Give not a windy night a rainy morrow,
To linger out a purposed overthrow.
If thou wilt leave me, do not leave me last,
When other petty griefs have done their spite,
But in the onset come; so shall I taste
At first the very worst of fortune's might;
 And other strains of woe, which now seem woe,
 Compared with loss of thee will not seem so.

So shall I live, supposing thou art true,
Like a deceivèd husband; so love's face
May still seem love to me, though altered new;
Thy looks with me, thy heart in other place:
For there can live no hatred in thine eye,
Therefore in that I cannot know thy change.
In many's looks, the false heart's history
Is writ in moods and frowns and wrinkles strange:
But heaven in thy creation did decree,
That in thy face sweet love should ever dwell;
Whate'er thy thoughts or thy heart's workings be,
Thy looks should nothing thence but sweetness tell.
 How like Eve's apple doth thy beauty grow,
 If thy sweet virtue answer not thy show.

They that have power to hurt and will do none,
That do not do the thing they most do show,
Who moving others, are themselves as stone,
Unmovèd, cold and to temptation slow;
They rightly do inherit heaven's graces
And husband nature's riches from expense;
They are the lords and owners of their faces,
Others but stewards of their excellence.
The summer's flower is to the summer sweet,
Though to itself it only live and die;
But if that flower with base infection meet,
The basest weed outbraves his dignity.
    For sweetest things turn sourest by their deeds;
    Lilies that fester smell far worse than weeds.

From you have I been absent in the spring,
When proud-pied April, dressed in all his trim,
Hath put a spirit of youth in everything,
That heavy Saturn laughed and leaped with him.
Yet nor the lays of birds nor the sweet smell
Of different flowers in odour and in hue
Could make me any summer's story tell
Or from their proud lap pluck them where they grew.
Nor did I wonder at the lily's white
Nor praise the deep vermilion in the rose;
They were but sweet, but figures of delight,
Drawn after you, you pattern of all those.
   Yet seemed it winter still and you away,
   As with your shadow I with these did play.

To me, fair friend, you never can be old,
For as you were when first your eye I eyed,
Such seems your beauty still. Three winters cold
Have from the forests shook three summers' pride,
Three beauteous springs to yellow autumn turned
In process of the seasons have I seen,
Three April perfumes in three hot Junes burned
Since first I saw you fresh, which yet are green.
Ah! yet doth beauty, like a dial hand,
Steal from his figure and no pace perceived;
So your sweet hue, which methinks still doth stand,
Hath motion and mine eye may be deceived:
    For fear of which, hear this, thou age unbred:
    Ere you were born was beauty's summer dead.

Let not my love be called idolatry
Nor my belovèd as an idol show,
Since all alike my songs and praises be
To one, of one, still such and ever so.
Kind is my love to-day, to-morrow kind,
Still constant in a wondrous excellence;
Therefore my verse to constancy confined,
One thing expressing, leaves out difference.
Fair, kind and true is all my argument,
Fair, kind and true, varying to other words;
And in this change is my invention spent,
Three themes in one, which wondrous scope affords.
    Fair, kind and true have often lived alone,
    Which three till now never kept seat in one.

When in the chronicle of wasted time
I see descriptions of the fairest wights
And beauty making beautiful old rhyme
In praise of ladies dead and lovely knights;
Then in the blazon of sweet beauty's best,
Of hand, of foot, of lip, of eye, of brow,
I see their antique pen would have expressed
Even such a beauty as you master now.
So all their praises are but prophecies
Of this our time, all you prefiguring,
And for they looked but with divining eyes,
They had not still enough your worth to sing;
   For we which now behold these present days
    Have eyes to wonder but lack tongues to praise.

Not mine own fears nor the prophetic soul
Of the wide world dreaming on things to come
Can yet the lease of my true love control,
Supposed as forfeit to a confined doom.
The mortal moon hath her eclipse endured
And the sad augurs mock their own presage;
Incertainties now crown themselves assured,
And peace proclaims olives of endless age.
Now with the drops of this most balmy time
My love looks fresh and death to me subscribes,
Since spite of him I'll live in this poor rhyme
While he insults o'er dull and speechless tribes.
 And thou in this shalt find thy monument
 When tyrants' crests and tombs of brass are spent.

What's in the brain that ink may character,
Which hath not figured to thee my true spirit?
What's new to speak, what new to register,
That may express my love or thy dear merit?
Nothing, sweet boy, but yet, like prayers divine,
I must each day say o'er the very same,
Counting no old thing old, thou mine, I thine,
Even as when first I hallowed thy fair name.
So that eternal love in love's fresh case
Weighs not the dust and injury of age
Nor gives to necessary wrinkles place,
But makes antiquity for aye his page,
    Finding the first conceit of love there bred
      Where time and outward form would show it dead.

O never say that I was false of heart
Though absence seemed my flame to qualify.
As easy might I from myself depart
As from my soul, which in thy breast doth lie.
That is my home of love; if I have ranged,
Like him that travels I return again,
Just to the time, not with the time exchanged,
So that myself bring water for my stain.
Never believe, though in my nature reigned
All frailties that besiege all kinds of blood,
That it could so preposterously be stained,
To leave for nothing all thy sum of good;
   For nothing this wide universe I call,
   Save thou, my rose; in it thou art my all.

Alas, 'tis true, I have gone here and there
And made myself a motley to the view,
Gored mine own thoughts, sold cheap what is most dear,
Made old offences of affections new.
Most true it is, that I have looked on truth
Askance and strangely. But by all above,
These blenches gave my heart another youth
And worse essays proved thee my best of love.
Now all is done, have what shall have no end:
Mine appetite I never more will grind
On newer proof, to try an older friend,
A god in love, to whom I am confined.
　　Then give me welcome, next my heaven the best,
　　Even to thy pure and most most loving breast.

Let me not to the marriage of true minds
Admit impediments. Love is not love
Which alters when it alteration finds
Or bends with the remover to remove.
O no, it is an ever-fixèd mark
That looks on tempests and is never shaken;
It is the star to every wandering bark,
Whose worth's unknown although his height be taken.
Love's not time's fool, though rosy lips and cheeks
Within his bending sickle's compass come.
Love alters not with his brief hours and weeks
But bears it out even to the edge of doom.
    If this be error and upon me proved,
    I never writ, nor no man ever loved.

What potions have I drunk of siren tears,
Distilled from limbecks foul as hell within,
Applying fears to hopes and hopes to fears,
Still losing when I saw myself to win!
What wretched errors hath my heart committed
Whilst it hath thought itself so blessèd never!
How have mine eyes out of their spheres been fitted
In the distraction of this madding fever!
O benefit of ill, now I find true
That better is by evil still made better
And ruined love, when it is built anew,
Grows fairer than at first, more strong, far greater.
    So I return rebuked to my content
    And gain by ill thrice more than I have spent.

That you were once unkind befriends me now
And for that sorrow which I then did feel
Needs must I under my transgression bow
Unless my nerves were brass or hammered steel.
For if you were by my unkindness shaken
As I by yours you've passed a hell of time
And I, a tyrant, have no leisure taken
To weigh how once I suffered in your crime.
O that our night of woe might have remembered
My deepest sense, how hard true sorrow hits,
And soon to you, as you to me then, tendered
The humble salve which wounded bosoms fits!
    But that your trespass now becomes a fee;
    Mine ransoms yours, and yours must ransom me.

'Tis better to be vile than vile esteemed
When not to be receives reproach of being
And the just pleasure lost, which is so deemed,
Not by our feeling, but by others' seeing.
For why should others' false adulterate eyes
Give salutation to my sportive blood?
Or on my frailties why are frailer spies,
Which in their wills count bad what I think good?
No, I am that I am and they that level
At my abuses reckon up their own;
I may be straight though they themselves be bevel.
By their rank thoughts my deeds must not be shown,
    Unless this general evil they maintain:
    All men are bad and in their badness reign.

Th' expense of spirit in a waste of shame
Is lust in action and till action, lust
Is perjured, murderous, bloody, full of blame,
Savage, extreme, rude, cruel, not to trust,
Enjoyed no sooner but despisèd straight,
Past reason hunted and no sooner had,
Past reason hated, as a swallowed bait,
On purpose laid to make the taker mad;
Mad in pursuit and in possession so,
Had, having and in quest to have, extreme:
A bliss in proof and proved, a very woe;
Before, a joy proposed; behind, a dream.
    All this the world well knows, yet none knows well
    To shun the heaven that leads men to this hell.

My mistress' eyes are nothing like the sun;
Coral is far more red than her lips' red;
If snow be white, why then her breasts are dun;
If hairs be wires, black wires grow on her head.
I have seen roses damasked, red and white,
But no such roses see I in her cheeks,
And in some perfumes is there more delight
Than in the breath that from my mistress reeks.
I love to hear her speak, yet well I know
That music hath a far more pleasing sound.
I grant I never saw a goddess go;
My mistress when she walks treads on the ground.
   And yet by heaven I think my love as rare
   As any she belied with false compare.

Beshrew that heart that makes my heart to groan
For that deep wound it gives my friend and me.
Is't not enough to torture me alone,
But slave to slavery my sweetest friend must be?
Me from myself thy cruel eye hath taken,
And my next self thou harder hast engrossed.
Of him, myself, and thee, I am forsaken;
A torment thrice threefold thus to be crossed.
Prison my heart in thy steel bosom's ward,
But then my friend's heart let my poor heart bail;
Whoe'er keeps me, let my heart be his guard;
Thou canst not then use rigour in my jail.
    And yet thou wilt, for I being pent in thee,
    Perforce am thine, and all that is in me.

So now I have confessed that he is thine
And I myself am mortgaged to thy will;
Myself I'll forfeit so that other mine
Thou wilt restore to be my comfort still.
But thou wilt not, nor he will not be free,
For thou art covetous and he is kind;
He learned but surety-like to write for me
Under that bond that him as fast doth bind.
The statute of thy beauty thou wilt take,
Thou usurer that put'st forth all to use,
And sue a friend came debtor for my sake;
So him I lose through my unkind abuse.
    Him have I lost, thou hast both him and me;
    He pays the whole and yet am I not free.

Two loves I have of comfort and despair,
Which like two spirits do suggest me still;
The better angel is a man right fair,
The worser spirit a woman coloured ill.
To win me soon to hell, my female evil
Tempteth my better angel from my side,
And would corrupt my saint to be a devil,
Wooing his purity with her foul pride.
And whether that my angel be turned fiend,
Suspect I may, yet not directly tell;
But being both from me, both to each friend,
I guess one angel in another's hell.
   Yet this shall I ne'er know, but live in doubt,
   Till my bad angel fire my good one out.

Poor soul, the centre of my sinful earth,
Thrall to these rebel powers that thee array,
Why dost thou pine within and suffer dearth,
Painting thy outward walls so costly gay?
Why so large cost, having so short a lease,
Dost thou upon thy fading mansion spend?
Shall worms, inheritors of this excess,
Eat up thy charge? Is this thy body's end?
Then, soul, live thou upon thy servant's loss,
And let that pine to aggravate thy store;
Buy terms divine in selling hours of dross;
Within be fed, without be rich no more.
　　So shalt thou feed on death, that feeds on men,
　　And death once dead, there's no more dying then.

My love is as a fever longing still
For that which longer nurseth the disease,
Feeding on that which doth preserve the ill,
Th' uncertain sickly appetite to please.
My reason, the physician to my love,
Angry that his prescriptions are not kept,
Hath left me and I desperate now approve
Desire is death, which physic did except.
Past cure I am, now reason is past care,
And frantic-mad with evermore unrest;
My thoughts and my discourse as madmen's are,
At random from the truth vainly expressed;
    For I have sworn thee fair and thought thee bright,
    Who art as black as hell, as dark as night.

O from what power hast thou this powerful might,
With insufficiency my heart to sway?
To make me give the lie to my true sight
And swear that brightness doth not grace the day?
Whence hast thou this becoming of things ill,
That in the very refuse of thy deeds
There is such strength and warrantise of skill,
That, in my mind, thy worst all best exceeds?
Who taught thee how to make me love thee more,
The more I hear and see just cause of hate?
O, though I love what others do abhor,
With others thou shouldst not abhor my state:
    If thy unworthiness raised love in me,
    More worthy I to be beloved of thee.

Index
of First Lines

Index of First Lines

About the Compiler

Lloyd Frankenberg is a well-known poet, critic, lecturer, and anthologist. A recipient of Guggenheim, Carnegie, Rockefeller, and Fulbright grants (among others), Mr. Frankenberg was director of poetry evenings at the Museum of Modern Art in New York City and originated a radio series entitled "What Is Poetry About?" on WNYC.

Mr. Frankenberg's poems have appeared in book form (THE RED KITE) and in numerous magazines and anthologies. He is the author of PLEASURE DOME: ON READING MODERN POETRY and has compiled three anthologies: INVITATION TO POETRY; A JAMES STEPHENS READER; and JAMES, SEUMAS AND JACQUES (unpublished writings of James Stephens).

In addition, he has edited a recording of PLEASURE DOME: AN AUDIBLE ANTHOLOGY OF MODERN POETRY READ BY ITS CREATORS, and to accompany INVITATION TO POETRY, he has recorded a selection of poems and comments under the title, A ROUND OF POEMS.

Mr. Frankenberg is married to the painter Loren MacIver and lives in New York City.

About the Illustrator

Nonny Hogrogian is well known for her ability to use a variety of techniques in her illustrations for children's books. She was awarded the Caldecott Medal for 1966 for her illustrations in the picture book *Always Room for One More*. In *Poems of William Shakespeare*, she turns to another medium, etchings.

Miss Hogrogian was born in New York City. She received a B.A. degree from Hunter College; she studied woodcutting and painting at The New School and graphics and weaving at the Haystack (Maine) Mountain School of Crafts.